AQA Mathematics

Exclusively endorsed and approved by AQA

Home

Series Editor
Paul Metcalf

Series Advisor
David Hodgson

Lead Author
Steven Lomax

June Haighton
Anne Haworth
Janice Johns
Andrew Manning
Kathryn Scott
Chris Sherrington
Margaret Thornton
Mark Willis

HIGHER
Modules 1 + 3

31869

Nelson Thornes
a Wolters Kluwer business

Published in 2006 by:
Nelson Thornes Ltd
Delta Place
27 Bath Road
CHELTENHAM
GL53 7TH
United Kingdom

06 07 08 09 10 / 10 9 8 7 6 5 4 3 2 1

A catalogue record for this book is available from the British Library.

ISBN 978 0 7487 8226 0

Cover photograph: Kingfisher by Paulo de Oliveira/OSF/Photolibrary
Page make-up by MCS Publishing Services Ltd, Salisbury, Wiltshire

Printed and bound in Spain by GraphyCems

Acknowledgements

The authors and publishers wish to thank the following for their contribution:
David Bowles for providing the Assess questions
David Hodgson for reviewing draft manuscripts

Thank you to the following schools:
Little Heath School, Reading
The Kingswinford School, Dudley
Thorne Grammar School, Doncaster

The publishers thank the following for permission to reproduce copyright material:

Vitruvian Man – Corel 481 (NT): p. 44

The publishers have made every effort to contact copyright holders but apologise if any have been overlooked.

Contents

Introduction

This book contains homework that allows you to practise what you have just learned. Each chapter is divided into sections that correspond to the numbered Learn topics for the matching chapter in the Students' Book.

 Means that these questions should be attempted with a calculator.

 Means that these questions are practice for the non-calculator paper in the exam and should be attempted without a calculator.

1 Underlined questions are harder questions.

1 Statistical measures

Homework 1

1 Write down the time you spend on each of these activities each week.

   a sleeping   **b** homework   **c** watching television

   Calculate the mean numbers of hours for each and write your answers to the nearest hour.

2 In a survey on the number of people in a household the following information was collected from 50 houses.

Number of people in a household	Number of households
1	9
2	19
3	9
4	8
5	4
6	1
Total	50

   a Find the mean, median, mode and range of household sizes.

   b Which average is the best one to use to represent the data? Explain your answer.

3 The graph shows the frequency of goals scored by a football team during a season.

a How many matches were played during the season?

b What is the modal score?

c What is the median number of goals scored?

d What is the mean score?

e What is the range of the number of goals scored?

4 Miss Saunders divided her class of 40 students into two groups, A and B.
She gave each group the same test which was marked out of 10.
The results are shown in the table below.

Number of marks	0	1	2	3	4	5	6	7	8	9	10
Group A frequency	3	0	0	5	1	6	1	2	0	0	0
Group B frequency	0	0	0	3	3	3	6	4	1	1	1

Which group did better?
Compare the two groups by finding the range and mean scores.

5 This bar chart shows the number of letters in words in a crossword puzzle.

Number of years' service	Number of teachers
0–4	11
5–9	15
10–14	4
15–19	10
20–24	6
25–30	4

Find the

a median   **b** mode   **c** mean   **d** range of the number of letters.

e Which average best represents the distribution?
Give a reason for your answer.

Homework 2

1   This table gives the number of years' service by 50 teachers at the Clare School.

Number of years' service	Number of teachers
0–4	11
5–9	15
10–14	4
15–19	10
20–24	6
25–30	4

a Find the modal class.

b Calculate an estimate of the mean.

2   In a science lesson, 30 runner bean plants were measured. Here are the results correct to the nearest centimetre.

6.2	5.4	8.9	12.1	6.5	9.3	7.2	12.7	10.2	5.4
7.7	9.5	11.1	8.6	7.0	13.5	12.7	5.6	15.4	12.3
13.4	9.5	6.7	8.6	9.1	11.5	14.2	13.5	8.8	9.7

The teacher suggested that the data was put into groups.

Length in centimetres	Tally	Total
5 but less than 7		
7 but less than 9		
9 but less than 11		
11 but less than 13		
13 but less than 15		
15 but less than 17		

a Copy and complete the table.

b Use the information to work out an estimate of the mean height of the plants.

c Calculate the mean from the original data.

d Why is your answer to part b only an estimate of the mean?

3   The heights of 50 students at Eastham School were measured.
The results were put into a table.

Height (h cm)	Frequency
$149.5 \leqslant h < 154.5$	4
$154.5 \leqslant h < 159.5$	21
$159.5 \leqslant h < 164.5$	18
$164.5 \leqslant h < 169.5$	7

Estimate the mean value of the distribution.

2 Representing data

Homework 1

1 Janesh undertakes a survey on packets of chocolate beans. He counts the number in each packet. His results are as follows:

30	31	30	30	29	32	41	29	30	31
30	28	30	31	30	30	30	30	31	30

a Show this information in a stem-and-leaf diagram.

b What is the most likely number of chocolate beans in a packet?

c Which number in the list is likely to be an error?

2 The prices paid for sandwiches in a canteen are shown below:

£3.25 £2.65 £3.15 £1.95 £2.85 £2.65 £3.25 £3.75 £1.95 £2.95

Copy and complete the following stem-and-leaf diagram to show this information.

Prices paid for sandwiches

Stem (£)	Leaf (pence)
1	
2	
3	

Key: 3|25 represents £3.25

3 The marks obtained in a test were recorded as follows.

11 22 20 19 25 18 12 9 27 22 10 18 24 16 15 22

a Show this information in an ordered stem-and-leaf diagram.

b What was the least number of marks in the test?

c Write down the mode of the marks in the test.

d Write down the range of the marks in the test.

4 The marks scored in a test by 15 boys and 15 girls is shown in this back-to-back stem-and-leaf diagram.

Number of marks in a test

Leaf (units) Girls	Stem (tens)	Leaf (units) Boys
9	0	6 7 8 9
9 8 6 5 4 2 0	1	1 3 4 5 5 5 7 8 9
7 6 4 3 2 1	2	2 4
0	3	

Key: 3|2 represents 23 marks

Key: 2|3 represents 23 marks

a Calculate the median for the girls.

b Calculate the mode for the boys.

c Calculate the mean for the girls.

d Calculate the range for the boys.

e What can you say about the performance of girls and boys?

5 Andy measures the resting heartbeat of 15 children and 15 adults. His results are recorded in the table.

Resting heartbeat														
Child 83	71	83	76	79	88	81	73	83	69	94	87	80	89	85
Adult 75	80	79	69	70	73	84	75	65	75	78	69	67	81	74

a Show this information in a back-to-back stem-and-leaf diagram.

b Andy says that 'the older you are, the slower your resting heartbeat'. Use your data to check Andy's hypothesis.

6 The table shows the results of a survey to find students' favourite pets.

Pet	Tally
Cat	⅃Ħ ⅃Ħ ⅃Ħ ⅃Ħ ⅃Ħ
Dog	⅃Ħ ⅃Ħ ⅃Ħ ⅃Ħ ⅃Ħ II
Horse	⅃Ħ ⅃Ħ IIII
Bird	⅃Ħ ⅃Ħ ⅃Ħ I
Fish	⅃Ħ III

Draw a pie chart to show the information.

7 Students at a college are asked to choose their favourite colour. Their choices are shown in the pie chart opposite:

A total of 45 students chose the colour blue.

a How many students were included in the survey?

b How many students chose red?

Twice as many students chose green as chose yellow.

c How many students chose green?

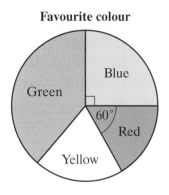

Favourite colour

Homework 2

1 The table shows the time spent waiting at a clinic.

Time, t (minutes)	Frequency
$0 \leqslant t < 10$	4
$10 \leqslant t < 20$	14
$20 \leqslant t < 30$	4
$30 \leqslant t < 40$	1

Draw a frequency diagram to represent the data.

2 The frequency diagram shows the ages of people in a church.

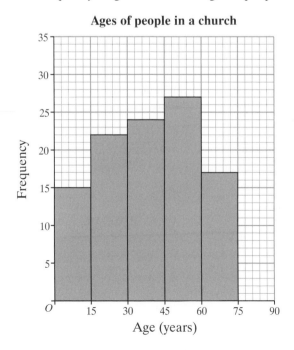

Ages of people in a church

7

Copy and complete this table to show this information.

Age, y (years)	Frequency
$0 \leqslant y < 15$	
$15 \leqslant y < 30$	
$30 \leqslant y < 45$	
$45 \leqslant y < 60$	
$60 \leqslant y < 75$	

3 The following table shows the temperature of a patient at different times of the day.

Time of day	10:00	11:00	12:00	13:00	14:00	15:00
Temperature (°F)	102.5	101.3	102	100.6	100.1	99.6

a Draw a line graph to show the temperature.

The normal temperature is 98.8 °F.

b At what time is the patient's temperature likely to return to normal?

4 The table shows the minimum and maximum temperatures at a seaside resort.

Day	Minimum temperature (°C)	Maximum temperature (°C)
Monday	15	19
Tuesday	17	22
Wednesday	14	21
Thursday	13	19
Friday	11	16

Draw a line graph to show:

a the minimum temperatures

b the maximum temperatures.

Use your graph to find:

c the day on which the lowest temperature was recorded

d the day on which the highest temperature was recorded.

5 **a** The table shows the quarterly phone bills for 2006 and 2007. The first two four-point moving averages are shown.

Copy the table and calculate the remaining four-point moving averages.

Year	2006	2006	2006	2006	2007	2007	2007	2007
Quarter	1st	2nd	3rd	4th	1st	2nd	3rd	4th
Cost	£115	£135	£103	£65	£101	£127	£43	£60
Four-point moving average		£104.50	£101.00					

b Show this information on a graph.

c What can you say about the trend?

6 Narinder's termly exam results are shown in the following table.

Year	2005	2006	2006	2006	2007	2007	2007
Session	Autumn	Spring	Summer	Autumn	Spring	Summer	Autumn
Results (%)	98	93	70	97	95	69	98

a Show this information on a graph.

b Use the information to calculate the three-point moving averages.

c Narinder says that her performance is improving. Is she correct? Give a reason for your answer.

7 The following table shows the mean number of sales of CDs and DVDs at a corner shop from 1998 to 2004.

Year	1998	1999	2000	2001	2002	2003	2004
CD sales	320	345	310	305	300	235	260
DVD sales	100	125	165	220	230	240	280

a Show this information on a graph.

b Construct a table showing the three-year moving average and plot the resulting trend lines.

c Comment on your results.

Homework 3

1   The table shows the heights of some trees.

Height (m)	Frequency
0 up to 2	6
2 up to 4	22
4 up to 8	15
8 up to 12	7

   a Show this information on a cumulative frequency diagram.

   b Use your cumulative frequency diagram to estimate:

      i the median

     ii the interquartile range.

2   The table shows the arm spans of students in a class.

Arm span (cm)	Frequency
$150 < l \leqslant 155$	3
$155 < l \leqslant 160$	9
$160 < l \leqslant 165$	13
$165 < l \leqslant 170$	17
$170 < l \leqslant 175$	8

   a Show this information in a cumulative frequency diagram.

   b Use your cumulative frequency diagram to estimate:

      i the median

     ii the interquartile range.

3   The table shows the wages of 40 staff in a small company.

Wages (£)	Frequency
$0 \leqslant x < 100$	5
$100 \leqslant x < 150$	11
$150 \leqslant x < 200$	15
$200 \leqslant x < 250$	7
$250 \leqslant x < 300$	0
$300 \leqslant x < 350$	2

   a Show this information on a cumulative frequency diagram.

   b Use your cumulative frequency diagram to estimate:

      i the median

     ii the interquartile range.

4 Andrea is completing her mathematics homework and draws this cumulative frequency diagram.

Cumulative frequency diagram

How can you tell that Andrea is wrong?
Give a reason for your answer.

5 Neil is comparing sentence lengths in newspapers and magazines, and has drawn this cumulative frequency diagram.

Newspaper and magazine sentence length

Which one has the longer sentences? Give a reason for your answer.

6 The waiting times at a dentist are recorded in the table below.

Time (min)	Frequency
$0 \leqslant t < 5$	8
$5 \leqslant t < 10$	12
$10 \leqslant t < 15$	7
$15 \leqslant t < 30$	3

   a Show this information on a cumulative frequency diagram.

   b Use your cumulative frequency diagram to estimate:

   i   the median

   ii the interquartile range

   iii the percentage of people waiting over 20 minutes.

7 The cumulative frequency diagram shows the time taken to complete a test.

Time taken to complete a test

Complete the table to show the cumulative frequency and frequency.

Time (min)	Cumulative frequency	Frequency
$0 < t \leqslant 5$		
$5 < t \leqslant 10$		
$10 < t \leqslant 15$		
$15 < t \leqslant 20$		
$20 < t \leqslant 25$		
$25 < t \leqslant 30$		

8 For each of these cumulative frequency diagrams, draw the associated frequency diagram as a line graph.

Cumulative frequency	Frequency diagram
a	
b	
c	
d	

Homework 4

1 Copy the box plot and write the correct labels in the spaces.

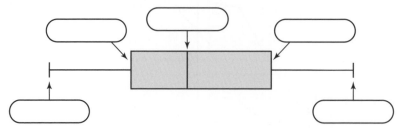

2 Draw a box plot of this data.

| 18 | 8 | 19 | 15 | 27 | 13 | 10 | 4 | 8 | 31 | 26 | 11 | 29 | 28 | 23 |

3 Draw a box plot of this data.

| 29 | 15 | 23 | 31 | 21 | 18 | 26 | 25 | 13 | 30 | 19 |

4 These box plots show the ages of shoppers in two clothes shops.

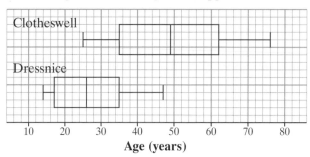

Copy and complete the table for the two shops.

	Clotheswell	Dressnice
Minimum age		
Maximum age		
Lower quartile		
Upper quartile		
IQR		
Median		
Range		

Compare the ages of the shoppers in the two shops.
What do you notice?

5 The cumulative frequency diagram shows the heights of 50 students.

a Use the cumulative frequency diagram to estimate:

  i the median

  ii the lower quartile

  iii the upper quartile.

b Draw a box plot for the data.

<u>6</u> Draw the cumulative frequency diagram for the data shown in each box plot.
In each case, use total frequency = 50

	Box plot	Cumulative frequency diagram
a		
b		
c		

Homework 5

1 The histogram gives the heights of bushes in a garden.

Histogram

a How many bushes are there in the garden?

b How many bushes have heights between 5 cm and 15 cm?

2 The table shows the distances travelled by van drivers.

Distance (miles)	Frequency
$0 < d \leqslant 10$	8
$10 < d \leqslant 20$	14
$20 < d \leqslant 30$	22
$30 < d \leqslant 50$	18
$50 < d \leqslant 100$	8

Show this information as:

a a histogram

b a frequency polygon.

3 The weights of 50 students are recorded as follows.

Weight (kg)	Frequency
$40 \leqslant w < 42.5$	1
$42.5 \leqslant w < 45$	10
$45 \leqslant w < 50$	16
$50 \leqslant w < 55$	13
$55 \leqslant w < 65$	9
$65 \leqslant w < 75$	1

Show this information as:

a a histogram

b a frequency polygon.

4 Light bulbs are tested to see how long they last. Here are the results of 60 tests.

Time (hours)	Frequency
$600 \leqslant x < 700$	3
$700 \leqslant x < 800$	15
$800 \leqslant x < 850$	20
$850 \leqslant x < 900$	12
$900 \leqslant x < 1000$	8
$1000 \leqslant x < 1200$	2

Draw a frequency polygon to show this information.

5 The cumulative frequency diagram shows the waiting times for 30 patients at a dentist. Show this information in a histogram.

Cumulative frequency diagram

Scatter graphs

Homework 1

1   The graph shows the marks awarded by two judges in a competition.

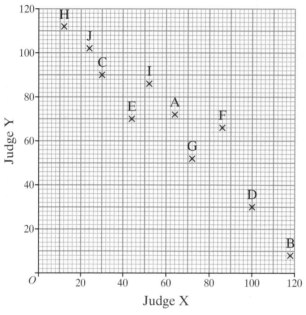

a Copy and complete the table for the marks awarded by the two judges.

	A	B	C	D	E	F	G	H	I	J
Judge X										
Judge Y										

b Are the two judges consistent? Give a reason for your answer.

2 For each of the following scatter graphs, match the diagram to the description.

a

i Strong positive correlation

b

ii Strong negative correlation

iii No correlation

c

iv Weak positive correlation

d

v Weak negative correlation

3 For each of the following data sets:

    i describe the type and strength of correlation

    ii write a sentence explaining the relationship between the two sets.

  a The age of a person and their IQ.

  b The number of cars on the road and the time taken to get home.

  c Age and value of a computer.

  d The distance to the destination and the cost of a holiday.

4 The scatter graph shows a comparison of the prices of paintings in 2000 and 2006.

Paintings

a Describe the type and strength of correlation.

b Write a sentence explaining the relationship between the two sets of data.

c Does the relation hold for all of the paintings? Give a reason for your answer.

5 The table shows the ages and second-hand values of eight cars.

Age of car (years)	3	1	4	7	12	9	8	2
Value of car (£)	2900	4000	2100	1200	300	500	1400	3500

a Draw a scatter graph of the results.

b Describe the type and strength of correlation.

c Write a sentence explaining the relationship between the two sets of data.

6 The table shows the rainfall and the number of raincoats sold at a department store.

Amount of rainfall (mm)	0	1	2	5	6	9	11
Number of raincoats sold	12	25	48	56	63	85	98

a Draw a scatter graph of the results.

b Describe the type and strength of correlation.

c Write a sentence explaining the relationship between the two sets of data.

7 The table shows the history and physics results for nine students.

History (%)	10	20	76	74	40	62	70	26	19
Physics (%)	75	82	15	23	51	33	18	64	78

a Draw a scatter graph of the results.

b Describe the type and strength of correlation.

c Write a sentence explaining the relationship between the two sets of data.

Homework 2

1 The table shows the ages and second-hand values of eight cars.

Age of car (years)	3	1	4	7	11	9	8	2
Value of car (£)	2900	4000	2100	1200	300	500	1400	3500

a Draw a scatter graph and a line of best fit of the results.

b Use your line of best fit to estimate:

i the value of a car if it is 10 years old

ii the age of a car if its value is £2000.

2 The table shows the rainfall and the number of raincoats sold at a department store.

Amount of rainfall (mm)	0	1	2	5	6	9	11
Number of raincoats sold	12	25	48	56	63	85	98

a Draw a scatter graph and a line of best fit of the results.

b Use your line of best fit to estimate:

i the number of raincoats sold for 8 mm of rainfall

ii the amount of rainfall if 50 raincoats are sold.

3 The table shows the history and physics results for nine students.

History (%)	10	20	76	74	40	62	70	26	19
Physics (%)	75	82	15	23	51	33	18	64	78

a Draw a scatter graph and a line of best fit of the results.

b Use your line of best fit to estimate:

i the physics result for a student who scores 54 in history

ii the history result for a student who scores 90 in physics.

c Which of these two answers is likely to be a better estimate? Give a reason for your answer.

4 The scatter graph shows a line of best fit for the science and maths results of eight students.

Science and maths results

a Use the line of best fit to estimate:

   i the maths result for a student who scores 60 in science

   ii the science result for a student who scores 100 in maths.

b Which of these two answers is likely to be a better estimate? Give a reason for your answer.

5 The table shows the engine sizes and maximum speeds of eight cars.

Engine size (cc)	Maximum speed (mph)
1100	80
1800	125
2900	142
1400	107
1300	96
1000	85
2500	135
2000	131

a Draw a scatter graph and the line of best fit of the results.

b Describe the relationship between a car's engine size and its maximum speed.

c Use your line of best fit to estimate:

   i the maximum speed of a car with an engine size of 1500 cc

   ii the engine size of a car whose maximum speed is 150 mph.

d Explain why your last answer might not be accurate.

6 A line of best fit shows the relationship between two sets of data in an experiment.

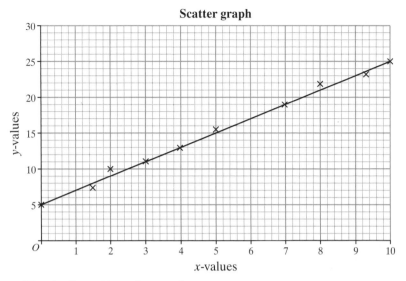

Scatter graph

a Use the line of best fit to estimate:

  i   the value of y when x = 7

  ii the value of x when y = 22.

b By considering the equation of the line of best fit, explain how you would find the value of y when x = 20.

7 The following table gives the age and speed of 15 people over a distance of 100 m.

Age (years)	12	5	8	10	11	12	15	14	18	28	34	38	42	39	33
Speed (m/s)	5.4	1.8	3.6	4.2	5.8	6.1	6.8	7.4	8.1	7.3	6.8	7.4	6.4	7.1	5.9

a Draw a scatter graph of the results.

b Draw a line of best fit for the results.

c Describe the relationship between speed and age.

d Find an estimate for the speed of someone aged 13 years.

4 Collecting data

Homework 1

1 For each of the following state whether the data is quantitative or qualitative.

   a Ages of people.

   b Favourite film ever!

   c Goals scored in a school hockey match.

   d Students' favourite teacher at a school.

   e The number of police at a football match.

   f The time it takes to get home.

   g The softness of a pile of towels.

2 For each of the following say whether the data is discrete or continuous.

   a Ages of people.

   b Goals scored in a school hockey match.

   c The number of votes in a council election.

   d The amount of water consumed by a household.

   e The viewing figures for a TV programme.

   f The time it takes to get home.

   g The number of stars that can be seen in the sky.

3 Connect each of the following to its proper description. The first one has been done for you.

Ages of lions at London Zoo	**Quantitative and discrete**
People's favourite cake at a show	
Points scored in 10 darts matches	
The weights of 12 newborn puppies	**Qualitative**
The favourite building of people in Britain	
The average speed of train journeys into London	
The number of hours spent driving a day	**Quantitative and continuous**
A person's shirt collar size	
The cost of bread	
Rainfall at a seaside resort	

4 The following questions are taken from different surveys.

Write down one criticism of each question.

Rewrite the question in a more suitable form.

a How many hours of homework do you complete each week?

Less than 1 hour ☐   More than 1 hour ☐

b What is your favourite colour?

Red ☐   Blue ☐

c How old are you?

Under 16 ☐   Under 21 ☐   Under 40 ☐

d You do like mathematics don't you?

Yes ☐   No ☐

e What is your favourite magazine?

Hello ☐   What car? ☐

5 Write down one advantage and one disadvantage of carrying out a personal (face-to-face) survey.

6 Write down a definition and give an example of each of the following kinds of data.

a Quantitative

b Qualitative

c Continuous

d Discrete

7 Give one advantage and one disadvantage of:

a primary data

b secondary data.

Homework 2

1 Which sampling methods are most appropriate for the following surveys?

Give a reason for each answer.

a The average weight of sheep on a farm with 1000 sheep.

b The favourite building of people in your town.

c The average amount of time spent on homework each week by students in your school.

d The average hand span of students in a school.

e The views of villagers on a new shopping centre.

f Information on voting intentions at a general election.

2 The following questions are taken from different surveys.

Write down one criticism of each question and explain how you would improve it.

a A company wants to find out if people like a new bar of chocolate they have made.

They stop people in the street and ask them to try it.

They give everyone a questionnaire asking them to write everything they like about the new bar.

b A London football club wants to build a new football stadium.

They carry out a survey in central London.

They ask 1000 people if they think it will be a good idea.

c Local commuters are trying to get an improved train service into London.

They collect signatures on the train one morning.

Three quarters of the respondents say that the train service could be improved.

d Jenny is collecting information on waiting times at her local health centre.

She gets permission from the doctors to undertake her survey.

She arrives one morning and makes a note of how long each patient waits.

e You want to find out if people like motor racing.

You carry out a face-to-face survey.

You ask 100 people watching the British Grand Prix at Silverstone.

f Tina is conducting a survey for the school magazine.

She wants to know about students' favourite colours for a new school uniform.

She asks 80 students from Year 7 and 70 students from Year 10 using random sampling.

3 A club wishes to undertake a survey of its members on whether to start serving food on the premises.

a Explain how you would take:

   i a convenience sample of 100 members

   ii a random sample of 100 members

   iii a stratified sample of 100 members.

b Which is the most appropriate sampling method?
Give a reason for your answer.

4 A police force employs 200 female and 2300 male police officers. They wish to take a sample of 140 police officers to see what they do in their spare time.

Explain how you would take:

a a random sample of 140 police officers

b a systematic sample of 140 police officers

c a stratified sample of 140 police officers.

d Which is the most appropriate sampling method? Give a reason for your answer.

5 Sally wishes to carry out a stratified sample of 80 people from students at her school.

Year	7	8	9	10	11
Number	120	150	150	180	200

How many students should she sample from each year group?

6 The table shows the number of people employed in a store.

Occupation	Management	Office	Security	Sales
Number	5	10	25	160

a Explain why a random sample of the employees might not be suitable.

b Explain how you would take a stratified sample of size 40.

c Explain how you would take a stratified sample of size 30.

5 Probability

Homework 1

Apart from question 4, this is a non-calulator exercise.

1 A coin is tossed 150 times. The result is 79 heads and 71 tails. Todd says, 'You should get equal numbers of heads and tails, so there's something wrong with that coin'.

Is he correct? Give a reason for your answer.

2 If the probability of getting an unwrapped toffee in a batch is 0.005, how many unwrapped toffees would you expect to find in a batch of 1000?

3 A spinner with nine equal divisions is spun 180 times. Three divisions are labelled X, two are Y, two are Z, one is P and one is Q.

a How many times would you expect the spinner to land on X?

b How many times would you expect it to land on Z?

c How many times would you expect it to land on Q?

 4 The probability that an inhabitant of Random Island is left-handed is $\frac{1}{8}$ There are 4263 people living on Random Island. How many of them would you expect to be left-handed?

5 The table shows the frequency distribution after choosing a card at random from a full pack 520 times.

	Results from 520 random choices		
	Picture card (J, Q, K)	Ace	Number card
Frequency distribution	119	44	357

a What is the relative frequency of getting an Ace?

b Using theoretical probability, how many Aces would you expect?

c Which one of the results in the table is the closest to the result you would expect from theoretical probability?

6 There are 3 yellow discs, 4 green discs and 5 black discs in a box. A disc is chosen at random and then put back. This is done 120 times. The table shows the frequency distribution.

	Results from choosing a disc 120 times		
	Yellow	**Green**	**Black**
Frequency distribution	33	39	48

  a What is the relative frequency of getting yellow?

  b What is the relative frequency of getting yellow or green?

  c What is the theoretical probability of getting black?

7 There are 50 counters in a bag. Some are blue, some are yellow and some are green. One counter is taken out at random and replaced. The frequency distribution table shows the results from 250 trials.

	Results from 250 trials		
	Blue	**Yellow**	**Green**
Frequency distribution	34	125	91

How many counters are there of each colour?

8 Sam has some coloured balls in a box. He asks his friends to pick a ball at random. He wants to find the probability of getting a yellow ball. After every ten attempts, he finds the relative frequency of yellow and the results are shown on the graph.

  a How many yellow balls had been picked after 10 attempts?

  b How many yellow balls had been picked after 50 attempts?

  c From the graph, estimate the probability of picking a yellow ball.

  d If there are 15 yellow balls, how many balls are in the bag altogether?

Homework 2

1 a Draw a table to show all the possible outcomes when four coins are tossed.

Use your table to find:

b the probability of getting four heads

c the probability of getting one head and three tails

d the probability of getting two heads and two tails

e the probability of getting at least one tail.

2 Kirsty has six tiles and two cards as shown in the diagram.

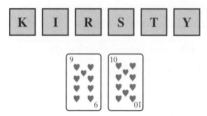

She takes one tile and one card at random.

a Draw a table of outcomes.

Use your table to find the probability that Kirsty takes:

b tile K and the 10 of hearts

c tile S or T and the 10 of hearts

d one of the tiles with a consonant and the 9 of hearts.

3 Two dice are thrown and the difference between their scores is recorded.

	1	2	3	4	5	6
1	0	1	2			
2						
3						
4						
5				1		
6				2		

a Copy and complete the sample space diagram.

Use your diagram to find:

b the probability of getting a difference of 4

c the probability of getting a difference of 6

d the probability of getting a difference greater than 4.

4 Gemma has the King, Queen and Jack of hearts plus the five tiles shown in the diagram.

She picks up one tile and one card at random.

a Draw a table of outcomes.

Use your table to find the probability that Gemma picks:

b the Jack and a tile with an E

c the Jack and a tile with an M.

5 Noah picks a card at random from a full pack. Harry picks a tile at random from a bag with five Hs and three Ys.
Find the probability that:

a Noah picks a heart and Harry picks a Y

b Noah picks a black card and Harry's tile is an H

c Noah does not pick a club and Harry does not pick a Y.

6 Jared has 20 marbles. Some are black, some are white and some are silver. He picks a marble at random. The probability that he will pick a black marble is 0.7 and the probability that he will pick a white marble is 0.25

a How many black marbles does he have?

b How many white marbles does he have?

c What is the probability that he will pick a silver marble?

7 A hexagonal spinner has sides numbered 2, 4, 6, 8, 10, 12. A second hexagonal spinner has sides numbered 1, 3, 5, 7, 9, 11. They are both spun and the product of their scores is recorded.

a Draw a sample space diagram.

Use your diagram to find:

b the probability of the product being an odd number

c the probability of the product being 18 or 36

d the probability of the product being a multiple of 5

e the probability of the product being at least 30.

8 Jodie throws three dice.

a How many possible outcomes are there?

b What is the probability that she gets a combined score of 18?

c What is the probability that she gets a combined score of 4?

Homework 3

1 Which of these are mutually exclusive events?

a Throwing a two and an even number on a throw of a dice.

b Throwing a number greater than three and an even number on a throw of a dice.

c Picking a heart and a Queen from a pack of cards.

d Picking the three of diamonds and the three of clubs from a pack of cards.

e Picking a red ball and picking a blue ball from a bag containing red, white and blue balls.

2 The probability that Marie will fail her history exam is $\frac{3}{20}$
What is the probability that she will pass the exam?

3 The probability that AQA Rovers will win their next match is 0.45
If the probability that they will draw is 0.25, what is the probability that they will lose?

4 Dilip can get into town in three different ways – with a lift from his father, by bus or walking. The probability that Dilip will get a lift is 0.65
The probability that he will catch the bus is 0.3
Baz says, 'That means there is a probability of 0.32 that he will walk'.
Explain why Baz is wrong and give the correct probability.

5 Restaurant Agaluxe has a menu with four choices.
The probability of each dish is shown below.

Dish	Probability
Steak	0.57
Chicken	0.33
Monkfish	0.15
Vegetarian	0.05

a How can you tell that the probabilities are incorrect?

b The first probability is incorrect.
What should it be?

6 Vicky goes out to buy some new jeans.
The probability that she buys them from Jeans'R'Us is $\frac{1}{4}$
The probability that she buys them from the Superstore is $\frac{5}{12}$
What is the probability that she buys them from one of these stores?

7 The probability that Jared will go to Leeds University is 0.45
The probability that he will go to Sheffield University is 0.25 and
the probability that he will go to Manchester University is 0.2

   a What is the probability that Jared will go to either Leeds or
Manchester?

   b What is the probability that he does not go to Manchester or
Sheffield?

   c What is the probability that he does not go to any of these three
universities?

8 Joanne has a box of fruit containing 8 apples, 11 pears, 6 oranges and
5 kiwi fruits. She takes a fruit from the box at random.

   a What is the probability that she takes a kiwi fruit?

   b What is the probability that she does *not* take an orange?

   c What is the probability that she takes either an apple or an orange?

9 Sam has a bag of 60 coloured marbles. Some are blue, some are green,
some are white and the rest are multi-coloured. Sam picks a marble at
random from the bag.
The probability that he will pick a blue marble is 0.15

   a How many blue marbles are in the bag?

The probability that he will *not* pick a green marble is 0.75

   b How many green marbles are in the bag?

Sam is twice as likely to pick a multi-coloured marble as a white one.

   c How many white marbles are in the bag?

10 Mr Mathsman has a collection of 250 books. Some are cookery books,
some are gardening books, 74 of them are travel books and the rest are
books about chess. He has three times as many gardening books as
cookery books. If one book is picked at random, the probability that it
will be a book about chess is 0.32

   a How many chess books does he have?

   b How many gardening books does he have?

Homework 4 🁢

Apart from question 8 this is a non-calculator exercise.

You may assume that the events described in this exercise are independent.

1 Karl takes a ball at random from a bag containing 2 red balls and 3 black ones. Errol throws a dice. What is the probability that:

   a Karl takes a red ball and Errol throws a six

   b Karl takes a black ball and Errol throws an odd number

   c Karl does not take a black ball and Errol does not throw a six?

2 There is a probability of 0.9 that Tanya will come top in the science exam and a probability of 0.4 that she will come top in geography. What is the probability that she comes top in both subjects?

3 The probability that Jan eats an egg for breakfast is $\frac{4}{5}$
   The probability that she cycles to school is $\frac{5}{6}$
   What is the probability that Jan eats an egg and cycles to school?

4 The probability that Dave gets into the rugby team is $\frac{3}{8}$
   The probability that he gets an A grade in his maths exam is $\frac{5}{6}$
   What is the probability that Dave gets into the rugby team but does not get an A grade in his maths exam?

5 Two dice are thrown together.
   What is the probability that both show an even number?

6 Five coins are tossed simultaneously.
   What is the probability that they all show heads?

7 If n coins are tossed simultaneously what is the probability that they all show heads?

🖩 **8** The probability that Jake will go to the gym in the evening is 0.6
   What is the probability that he goes to the gym on Monday, Tuesday and Thursday evenings but not Wednesday evening?

9 Pippa, Roz and Sally are all taking their ballet exam next week.
The probability that Pippa will pass is $\frac{2}{3}$
The probability that Roz will pass is $\frac{3}{4}$
The probability that Sally will pass is $\frac{5}{6}$

    a Tara says that the probability that they will all pass is $\frac{2}{3} + \frac{3}{4} + \frac{5}{6} = \frac{27}{12}$

       i Why should Tara know that her answer must be wrong?

      ii What is the correct answer?

    b What is the probability that Pippa and Sally will pass but Roz will fail?

    c What is the probability that they will all fail?

Homework 5

1 The probability that Aisha will pass her piano exam is 0.9 and the
probability that Sean will pass his clarinet exam is 0.7

    a Copy and complete the tree diagram.

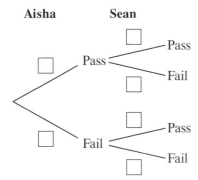

Use it to find:

    b the probability that both of them pass their exams

    c the probability that Aisha fails and Sean passes

    d the probability that at least one of them fails.

2 A box contains 7 blue pens and 9 black pens. One pen is taken from the
box and then replaced. A second pen is then taken from the box.

    a Draw a tree diagram.

Use it to find:

    b the probability that both pens are blue

    c the probability that the first pen is blue and the second pen is black

    d the probability that one pen is blue and one is black.

3 Do question **2** again on the basis that the first pen is *not* replaced.

4 There are six brown eggs and six white eggs in a box. Two eggs are taken at random. Find the probability that:

a they are both white

b one egg is brown and one is white.

5 A box contains 15 milk chocolates and 10 dark chocolates. Imogen takes a chocolate at random and eats it. If it is milk chocolate, she will take another one. If it is dark chocolate, she will stop. Find the probability that Imogen takes:

a two milk chocolates

b two dark chocolates.

6 The probability that Tara's Mum will pack her lunch box overnight is 0.8
If Tara finds her lunchbox already packed, the probability that she will get to school on time is 0.9, but if Tara has to pack her own lunch box, the probability that she will be on time is 0.4
Find the probability that Tara is late for school.

7 The probability that Frazer will go swimming on Saturday is $\frac{4}{5}$
If he goes swimming, the probability that he will go for a run is $\frac{1}{4}$
If he does not go swimming, the probability that he goes for a run is $\frac{5}{6}$
Find the probability that Frazer does not go for a run on Saturday.

8 Paula is going to France for a holiday. She can travel by ferry, plane or rail. The probability that she goes by ferry is 0.2 and the probability that she goes by plane is 0.45

If Paula goes by ferry, the probability that she stays a night in Paris is 0.8, but if she goes by plane, the probability that she stays a night in Paris is 0.3

If she goes by rail, the probability that she stays a night in Paris is 0.5

Find the probability that:

a Paula goes by ferry but does not stay in Paris

b she goes by rail and stays in Paris

c she stays in Paris.

9 Joe has 4 plain white socks, 8 grey socks and 12 patterned socks in his drawer. He takes out one sock and then another.

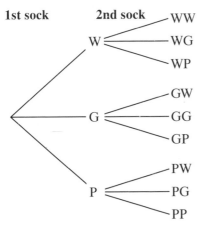

1st sock   **2nd sock**

W — WW
W — WG
W — WP

G — GW
G — GG
G — GP

P — PW
P — PG
P — PP

a Copy and complete the tree diagram.

Find:

b the probability that Joe has picked two patterned socks

c the probability that he has picked one white and one grey sock

d the probability that he has picked a pair of matching socks.

10 Box A contains one black ball, one pink ball, one yellow ball, one blue ball and one green ball. Box B contains one black ball, one pink ball, one yellow ball, one blue ball and two white balls. One ball is picked at random from box A and placed in box B. A ball is then picked at random from box B.

Calculate the probability that:

a the ball picked from box A is blue and the ball picked from box B is also blue

b the ball picked from box A and the ball picked from box B are the same colour.

1 Integers

Homework 1

1. Write all the factors of these numbers.

   a 16   **b** 24   **c** 60   **d** 100

2. Write the first five multiples of these numbers.

   a 4   **b** 10   **c** 14

3. Find the least common multiple (LCM) of each set of numbers.

   a 2 and 7   **c** 4 and 5   **e** 4, 6 and 9

   b 5 and 3   **d** 8 and 5

4. Find the highest common factor (HCF) of each set of numbers.

   a 8 and 12   **c** 12 and 18   **e** 48 and 72

   b 8 and 18   **d** 24 and 30

5. Look at these numbers:

   2, 3, 4, 5, 6, 7, 8, 9, 10, 11, 12, 13, 14, 15

   a Which are factors of 12?

   b Which are multiples of 6?

   c Which are factors of 15?

   d Which are multiples of 4?

6. **Get Real!**
   Two buses stop at the same bus stop.
   On one route the bus stops every 25 minutes.
   On the other route the bus stops every 40 minutes.
   If both buses leave the stop at 9 a.m., at what time should the buses next reach the stop together?

7. One light flashes every 8 seconds.
   A second light flashes every 10 seconds and a third every 15 seconds.
   If the three lights start flashing at the same time, after how long will they flash together again?

8 In a 10 000 m race, one runner is taking 64 seconds a lap.
Another runner takes 72 seconds a lap.
After how many laps will the faster runner first lap the slower runner?

Homework 2

1 Write the following numbers as products of prime factors.

   a 52   **b** 60   **c** 44   **d** 64   **e** 80

2 Express each number as a product of its prime factors.
Write your answers using index notation.

   a 70   **b** 96   **c** 100   **d** 150   **e** 256

3 Write 126 as a product of prime factors.

4 p and q are prime numbers. Find the values of p and q when $p^3 \times q = 24$.

5 What numbers are these?

   a It is a prime number. It is a factor of 91. It is not a factor of 26.

   b It is a prime number. It is a factor of 132. It is bigger than 5.

6 Look at this set of numbers.

   8   37   73   91   180   270   360

   a Which two numbers are prime numbers?

   b Which number can be written in index form as $2^3 \times 3^2 \times 5$?

7 What are the prime factors of 1000?
Write your answer using index notation.

8 A number expressed as a product of its prime factors is $2^6 \times 3^4 \times 5^2$.
What is the number?

9 Express these numbers in prime factors. Hence, find their
   i highest common factor (HCF)   **ii** least common multiple (LCM)

   a 28, 16   **b** 64, 24   **c** 80, 48

Homework 3

Apart from question 6, this is a non-calculator exercise.

1 Find the reciprocal of these numbers.

   a 2   **b** 9   **c** 6   **d** 15

2 Find the reciprocal of these numbers.

   a $\frac{1}{3}$ **b** $\frac{1}{14}$ **c** $\frac{1}{11}$ **d** $\frac{2}{5}$

3 What is the value of $1 \div \frac{1}{4}$?

4 Find the reciprocal of these numbers.

   a 0.2   **b** 0.75   **c** 0.6   **d** $0.\dot{6}$

5 Find the reciprocal of these numbers.

   a $3\frac{1}{5}$ **b** $6\frac{7}{8}$ **c** $2\frac{3}{5}$ **d** $4\frac{9}{10}$

6 Find the reciprocals of the numbers from 30 to 40.
Write them to 4 decimal places if they are not exact decimals.
Which of the numbers have reciprocals that are:

   a exact decimals

   b decimals with one recurring figure

   c decimals with two recurring figures

   d decimals with three recurring figures?

2 Rounding

Do not use your calculator for estimating!
You may, though, want to check your answers with the help of your calculator.

1 For each question, decide which estimate is best.

		Estimate A	Estimate B	Estimate C
a	3.67 × 7.4	2.8	2.1	28
b	1.8 × 21.4	4	40	400
c	12.34 ÷ 4.1	3	0.3	48
d	51.5 × 9.8	5	50	500
e	6.1 ÷ 2.1	0.3	3	30
f	44.1 × 1.8	80	44	440
g	6.8 ÷ 1.1	7	70	0.7
h	2.8 × 4.2 ÷ 3.8	3	2	1
i	31.9 ÷ 6.2 × 3.2	2	150	15

2 For each pair of calculations, estimate the answers to help you decide which you think will have the larger answer.

a 4.2×2.8 or 5.1×2.3

c $13.41 - 4.28$ or $27.5 \div 2.14$

b $33.3 \div 6.2$ or 2.31×2.78

d 59.4×31.6 or 95.3×9.8

3 Estimate the answers to these calculations by rounding to one significant figure.

a $8.6 + 4.9$

e 0.2×6

i $\dfrac{89.8 \times 5.9}{0.32}$

m $23.9(5.35 - 2.79)$

b $7.9 \div 2.1$

f $\dfrac{52.1 \times 4.7}{4.8}$

j $23.9(5.35 + 2.79)$

c $59.1 + 40.8$

g $\dfrac{33.7 + 53.2}{77.1 - 68.5}$

k $\dfrac{38.2 \times 7.9}{0.48}$

d 9.1×8.8

h $\dfrac{3.6 \times 7.1}{0.11}$

l $\dfrac{89.8 + 5.9}{0.32}$

4 a Write down two consecutive whole numbers, one that is smaller than the square root of 40 and one that is larger.

   b Write down two consecutive whole numbers, one that is smaller than the square root of 120 and one that is larger.

5 Estimate 6.32 + 4.26 by rounding to the nearest whole number.

   Explain why the answer is an underestimate of the exact answer.

6 A group of 29 people weigh a total of 2772 kg.

   Estimate their mean weight.

   Is this a reasonable amount for the mean weight of a large number of people?

7 Estimate the total cost of 58 computers at £885 each.

8 Estimate the square roots of these numbers.

   a 15   **b** 30   **c** 60   **d** 5   **e** 2000

9 Estimate 4.13 × 8.22 by rounding to one significant figure.

   Explain why the answer is an underestimate of the exact answer.

10 Joe estimated the answer to 12.2 ÷ 8.2 as 1.5 by rounding both numbers down. Does this mean that 1.5 is an underestimate of the correct answer?

11 Explain why 2.4 ÷ 0.6 has the same answer as 24 ÷ 6 and 240 ÷ 60.

12 Which of these make a number larger and which of them make it smaller?

   a Dividing by 10   **c** Dividing by 0.1

   b Multiplying by 10   **d** Multiplying by 0.1

13 Estimate the answers to:

   a 41 ÷ 8.2   **b** 41 ÷ 0.82   **c** 41 ÷ 0.082

14 a Find five numbers whose square roots are between 9 and 10.

   b Find two consecutive whole numbers to complete this statement:

      'The square root of 70 is between ... and ...'

15 Get Real!
   Estimate the total cost of five CDs costing £6.98 each.

16 Estimate how many bottles of water costing 47 pence each you can buy for £8.

17 Estimate how much fencing is needed for a rectangular field measuring 48.5 m by 63 m.

18 A group of nine people wins £4855 on the lottery.
Estimate how much each person will get when the money is shared out equally.

<u>19</u> Matt drives at an average speed of 57.8 miles an hour for 2 hours 55 minutes.
Estimate how far he goes.

Homework 2

1 Each of these quantities is rounded to the nearest whole number of units. Write down the minimum and maximum possible size of each quantity.

   a 26 g   **c** 225 m   **e** 33 kg

   b 4 cm   **d** 13 litres   **f** £249

2 The upper bound of a length measured to three significant figures is 3.295 m.

If the actual length is x metres, copy and complete this statement:
... $\leqslant x <$ ... .

<u>3</u> Get Real!
A man is allowed to carry loads up to a total of 25 kg. He is asked to carry 12 packets weighing 2 kg each, measured correct to the nearest 100 g. Can he complain about this? Explain your reasoning.

4 The amount of breakfast cereal in a packet is designed to be 510 g with an acceptable limit of 2 per cent either way. What is the minimum possible weight of cereal in the packet?

5 The weight of a toffee is 5 g correct to the nearest half gram.
What is the minimum possible weight of 100 of these toffees?

3 Decimals

1 Work out:

    a 3.2×3.2 **c** 3.2×0.52 **e** 4.6×7.8 **g** 0.67×0.43

    b 4.2×1.4 **d** 4.2×9.1 **f** 5.6×3.4 **h** 0.345×0.03

2 Using your answers to question **1**, write down the answers to these
multiplications.

    a 3.2×0.32 **c** 32×0.52 **e** 4.6×0.078 **g** 67×0.43

    b 4.2×0.14 **d** 0.42×0.91 **f** 0.0056×3.4 **h** 34.5×30

3 Neeta knows $4 \times 7 = 28$. She says that $0.4 \times 0.7 = 0.28$

Joe says $0.4 \times 0.7 = 2.8$

Who is right? Explain your answer.

4 You can split 8 into two parts, 2 and 6. Then multiply: $2 \times 6 = 12$

You can split 8 into two parts, 3 and 5. Then multiply: $3 \times 5 = 15$

Split 8 into two parts and multiply them together. Your aim is to get
close to 14. How close can you get? (You will need to use decimals.)

5 A palindrome reads the same forwards as backwards.

So 4.2×2.4 is a palindrome. So is 1.5×5.1

    a Which is bigger, 4.2×2.4 or 1.5×5.1?

    b Which is bigger, 6.2×2.6 or 3.5×5.3?

    c Which is bigger, 9.2×2.9 or 7.4×4.7?

In parts **a–c**, the two numbers have the same sum.

For example, in part **a**, $4.2 + 2.4 = 1.5 + 5.1$

    d Here are two more. Can you predict which will have the bigger answer
before you work them out?

        i 7.2×2.7 or 4.5×5.4

        ii 5.7×7.5 or 3.9×9.3

    e Can you find any multiplications with a palindromic answer,
for example, $3.3 \times 3.7 = 12.21$?

Homework 2

1 Work out $414 \div 6$

2 Use your answer to question **1** to work these out:

   a $41.4 \div 6$ **b** $4.14 \div 0.6$ **c** $0.414 \div 0.06$ **d** $414 \div 0.6$

3 Eight friends go out for a meal. The total cost is £100.32
They decide to split the cost equally between them.

   How much should they each pay?

4 Work out:

   a $2.45 \div 0.5$ **c** $2.34 \div 0.8$ **e** $9.65 \div 0.5$ **g** $8.765 \div 0.1$

   b $9.12 \div 0.6$ **d** $9.6 \div 0.12$ **f** $24.97 \div 1.1$ **h** $0.005 \div 0.4$

5 Get Real!

The Healthy Bite Café buys orange juice in big containers. Each
container holds 15 litres of juice.

   a How many 0.3 litre cups can they get from a 15 litre container?

   b If they charge £0.85 for each cup, how much money do they get from all
these cups?

   c They pay £23.85 for a big container. How much profit do they make?

6 Get Real!

Aisha goes to the supermarket and sees some bottles of squash on offer
at £1.10 each. She has £30 in her pocket.

   a How many bottles can she buy?

   b Work out the exact cost of these bottles.

   c How much change will she have left?

7 Work out:

   a $4.96 \div 1.6$ **c** $0.51 \div 1.5$ **e** $7.263 \div 1.8$

   b $7.222 \div 2.3$ **d** $21.06 \div 2.6$ **f** $0.02 \div 400$

8 If $2.6 \times 3.3 = 8.58$, write down the answer to:

   a $8.58 \div 0.33$ **b** $85.8 \div 26$ **c** $0.858 \div 26$ **d** $85.8 \div 0.033$

Homework 3

Apart from question 7, this is a non-calculator exercise.

1 Change these decimals to fractions.

    a 0.7   **b** 0.35   **c** 0.85   **d** 0.26   **e** 0.375   **f** 0.325

2 Change these fractions to decimals.

    a $\frac{2}{5}$ **b** $\frac{3}{10}$ **c** $\frac{7}{20}$ **d** $\frac{5}{8}$

3 Change these fractions to recurring decimals.

    a $\frac{2}{3}$ **b** $\frac{5}{6}$ **c** $\frac{2}{7}$ **d** $\frac{5}{12}$

4 James thinks 0.38 is the same as $\frac{3}{8}$

    a Is James correct?
       Give a reason for your answer.

    b Which is bigger, 0.38 or $\frac{3}{8}$?

    c How much bigger? Give your answer as a fraction and a decimal.

5 **a** Change 0.5 and 0.05 to fractions.

    b Now change 0.6 and 0.06 to fractions.

    c What do you notice?

    d If $0.65 = \frac{13}{20}$, what decimal do you think is equal to $\frac{13}{200}$?

6 If $\frac{3}{8} = 0.375$, what is the decimal equivalent of

    a $\frac{3}{80}$ **b** $\frac{6}{80}$ **c** $\frac{3}{16}$?

7 **a** Use a calculator to change these fractions to decimals.

    i $\frac{1}{9}$ **ii** $\frac{12}{99}$ **iii** $\frac{123}{999}$

    b There is a pattern in the questions, and a pattern in the answers.
      Use the patterns to predict a fraction which is equal to
      0.12345123451234512345 ...

      Check you are right by changing your answer to a decimal.

Homework 4

 1 Write the following recurring decimals as fractions.

   a $0.\dot{1}$ **b** $0.\dot{1}\dot{2}$ **c** $0.\dot{1}2\dot{3}$?

 2 Change these fractions into recurring decimals.

   a $\frac{5}{11}$ **b** $\frac{7}{111}$

 3 Find a fraction that is equal to:

   a $0.3\dot{6}$ **b** $0.\dot{3}\dot{6}$

 4 Barry says that $\frac{4}{7} = 0.57142\dot{8}$

   Harry says that $\frac{4}{7} = 0.\dot{5}7142\dot{8}$

   Larry says that $\frac{4}{7} = 0.\dot{5}71428\dot{5}$

   Who is right?

   Give a reason for your answer.

 5 It is easy to find decimals with one recurring digit, or two recurring digits. What other numbers of recurring digits can you find, and what fractions lead to them?

 6 The Fibonnaci sequence starts 1, 1, 2, 3, 5, 8, 13, ...

   a Key this sequence into your calculator:

   $1 \times 10 = \times 10 + 1 \times 10 = \times 10 + 2 \times 10 = \times 10 + 3 \times 10 = ...$

   These numbers are the Fibonacci sequence.

   Write down the display each time you press the $\boxed{=}$ key.

   b Work out the recurring decimal for $\frac{1}{89}$

   c What do you notice about your answers?

4 Fractions

You should be able to do all of these without a calculator but make sure you know how to use a calculator to check your work or to speed it up.

1 Work out:

a $\frac{3}{10} + \frac{2}{15}$ **b** $\frac{3}{10} - \frac{2}{15}$ **c** $\frac{4}{5} + \frac{3}{8}$ **d** $\frac{4}{5} - \frac{3}{8}$

2 Work out:

a $2\frac{3}{10} + 1\frac{2}{15}$ **b** $2\frac{3}{10} - 1\frac{2}{15}$ **c** $3\frac{1}{4} + 1\frac{1}{3}$ **d** $3\frac{1}{3} - 1\frac{1}{4}$

3 Work out:

a $2\frac{2}{15} + 1\frac{3}{10}$ **b** $2\frac{2}{15} - 1\frac{3}{10}$ **c** $3\frac{1}{3} + 1\frac{1}{4}$ **d** $4\frac{1}{4} - 1\frac{2}{3}$

4 How many times does $\frac{2}{3}$ go into 4? (Work this out by repeatedly subtracting $\frac{2}{3}$ from 4.)

5 Find the sum of $1\frac{2}{3}$ and $2\frac{1}{5}$

6 **a** John says, 'When you double $2\frac{1}{2}$ you get $4\frac{1}{4}$.'
Is John right? Show how you worked out your answer.

    b Lynn says, '$\frac{4}{5}$ plus $\frac{1}{3}$ is $\frac{5}{8}$.'
Is Lynn right? Show how you worked out your answer.

7 Without working out the answers, arrange these calculations in order, the one with the smallest answer first and the one with the largest answer last.

$1 + \frac{2}{3}$ $1 - \frac{2}{3}$ $1 + \frac{4}{3}$ $1 - \frac{4}{3}$

8 Find three different pairs of fractions that add up to 6.

9 **Get Real!**
David's recipe says that he needs two thirds of a cup of cream for some ice cream for four people. How much cream does he need if he wants to make ice cream for eight people?

10 Get Real!

Diane is making hats and bags for a school sale.

Each hat needs $\frac{3}{8}$ of a yard of fabric and each bag needs $\frac{2}{3}$ of a yard.

How much fabric is needed to make a hat and bag set?

Homework 2

1 Work out:

a $15 \times \frac{1}{5}$ **c** $36 \times \frac{2}{3}$ **e** $15 \times \frac{4}{5}$ **g** $36 \times \frac{5}{9}$

b $26 \times \frac{1}{2}$ **d** $45 \times \frac{2}{9}$ **f** $26 \times \frac{1}{4}$ **h** $45 \times \frac{3}{10}$

2 Work out:

a $\frac{4}{5} \times \frac{1}{2}$ **c** $\frac{3}{4} \times \frac{1}{3}$ **e** $\frac{7}{9} \times \frac{3}{7}$ **g** $\frac{2}{3} \times \frac{5}{8}$

b $\frac{1}{2} \times \frac{5}{8}$ **d** $\frac{3}{10} \times \frac{2}{15}$ **f** $\frac{4}{9} \times \frac{9}{10}$ **h** $\frac{9}{16} \times \frac{5}{9}$

3 Work out:

a $2 \div \frac{1}{7}$ **c** $12 \div \frac{1}{6}$ **e** $8 \div \frac{2}{3}$ **g** $18 \div \frac{3}{4}$

b $5 \div \frac{1}{4}$ **d** $45 \div \frac{5}{9}$ **f** $10 \div \frac{5}{8}$ **h** $32 \div \frac{4}{5}$

4 Work out:

a $\frac{5}{6} \div \frac{1}{3}$ **c** $\frac{7}{10} \div \frac{3}{5}$ **e** $\frac{2}{7} \div \frac{4}{7}$ **g** $\frac{9}{25} \div \frac{3}{5}$

b $\frac{5}{8} \div \frac{1}{4}$ **d** $\frac{2}{7} \div \frac{2}{7}$ **f** $\frac{2}{7} \div \frac{1}{7}$ **h** $\frac{4}{15} \div \frac{2}{3}$

5 Jared says that $\frac{3}{4} \div \frac{1}{2} = \frac{3}{8}$

Is he correct? Explain your answer.

6 Yasmin and Zoe are working out $\frac{9}{10} \times \frac{5}{6}$

Yasmin says the answer is $\frac{45}{60}$

Zoe says the answer is $\frac{3}{4}$

Who is correct? Explain your answer.

7 Lyn says, '6 divided by $\frac{1}{3}$ is 2.'

Is Lyn correct? Explain your answer.

8 Without working out the answers, arrange these calculations in order, the one with the smallest answer first and the one with the largest answer last.

$1 \times \frac{1}{3}$ $1 \div \frac{1}{3}$ $1 \times \frac{2}{3}$ $1 \div \frac{2}{3}$

9 Get Real!

David's recipe says that he needs two thirds of a cup of cream for some ice cream for four people. How much cream does he need if he wants to make ice cream for six people?

10 Get Real!

Diane has 4 yards of fabric to make some hats for a school sale. Each hat needs $\frac{3}{8}$ yard of fabric. How many hats can Diane make and how much fabric is left over?

5 Surds

1 Write these numbers in the form $\frac{a}{b}$, giving your answers in their lowest terms.

    a 0.8   **b** 11   **c** $3\frac{1}{4}$ **d** $0.\dot{7}$ **e** $0.\dot{1}6\dot{2}$

2 Which of these are rational, and which are irrational?

    a $\sqrt{2}$ **c** $\dfrac{\sqrt{10}}{11}$ **e** $\sqrt{10}+\sqrt{10}$

    b $\sqrt{49}$ **d** $\sqrt{10}\times\sqrt{10}$ **f** $\dfrac{\sqrt{12}}{\sqrt{3}}$

3 Simplify:

    a $\sqrt{27}$ **b** $\sqrt{63}$ **c** $\sqrt{32}$ **d** $\sqrt{147}$

4 Simplify:

    a $5\sqrt{2}+\sqrt{2}$ **c** $\sqrt{20}-\sqrt{5}$ **e** $\sqrt{50}-\sqrt{18}$ **g** $\sqrt{75}+\sqrt{27}$

    b $9\sqrt{5}-\sqrt{5}$ **d** $\sqrt{27}+\sqrt{3}$ **f** $6\sqrt{3}-\sqrt{48}$ **h** $\sqrt{12}+3\sqrt{3}-\sqrt{48}$

5 Jamilah says $4\times3\sqrt{2}=12\sqrt{8}=12\times2\sqrt{2}=24\sqrt{2}$. Josef says $4\times3\sqrt{2}=12\sqrt{2}$.
Who is wrong, and where is the mistake?

6 Simplify:

    a $\sqrt{6}\times\sqrt{12}$ **c** $4\sqrt{3}\times3\sqrt{6}$ **e** $\dfrac{5\sqrt{10}}{\sqrt{5}}$ **g** $\sqrt{2}(4+\sqrt{8})$

    b $\sqrt{14}\times2\sqrt{7}$ **d** $\dfrac{\sqrt{20}}{\sqrt{5}}$ **f** $\sqrt{5}(2+\sqrt{5})$ **h** $(3+\sqrt{3})(2+\sqrt{3})$

7 Which of these are correct, and which are incorrect?

    a $\sqrt{6}+\sqrt{2}=\sqrt{8}=2\sqrt{2}$ **c** $\sqrt{6}\div\sqrt{2}=\sqrt{3}$

    b $\sqrt{6}\times\sqrt{2}=\sqrt{12}=2\sqrt{3}$ **d** $\sqrt{6}-\sqrt{2}=\sqrt{4}=2$

8 A cube has a total surface area of 48 cm². Find:

   a the surface area of one face

   b the length of an edge of the cube, giving your answer in its simplified surd form.

9 Find the odd one out in each row.

   a i $\sqrt{20}$ **ii** $2\sqrt{5}$ **iii** $\dfrac{\sqrt{40}}{2}$ **iv** $\sqrt{45} - \sqrt{5}$

   b i $\dfrac{\sqrt{30}}{\sqrt{3}}$ **ii** $\sqrt{12} - \sqrt{2}$ **iii** $\sqrt{2} \times \sqrt{5}$ **iv** $\dfrac{\sqrt{40}}{2}$

   c i $\sqrt{\dfrac{40}{5}}$ **ii** $\dfrac{2\sqrt{5} + 2\sqrt{5}}{\sqrt{5}}$ **iii** $\sqrt{2} + \sqrt{2}$ **iv** $\dfrac{2\sqrt{6}}{\sqrt{3}}$

10 Write $\sqrt{50} + \sqrt{18}$ in the form $a\sqrt{b}$.

Homework 2

1 Rationalise the denominators of these fractions:

   a $\dfrac{2}{\sqrt{3}}$ **c** $\dfrac{4}{2\sqrt{3}}$ **e** $\dfrac{3\sqrt{2}}{\sqrt{6}}$ **g** $\sqrt{\dfrac{5}{11}}$

   b $\dfrac{6}{\sqrt{3}}$ **d** $\dfrac{3\sqrt{5}}{5\sqrt{3}}$ **f** $\dfrac{3\sqrt{6}}{2\sqrt{3}}$ **h** $\dfrac{7\sqrt{7}}{2\sqrt{14}}$

2 Show that $\dfrac{3}{\sqrt{3}} = \sqrt{3}$.

3   Find your way through this maze, only occupying spaces where the answer is correct.

Start	$\dfrac{2}{\sqrt{5}} = \dfrac{\sqrt{5}}{5}$	$\dfrac{3}{2\sqrt{3}} = \dfrac{\sqrt{3}}{3}$	$\sqrt{\dfrac{4}{9}} = \dfrac{2}{3}$	**End**
$\dfrac{1}{\sqrt{5}} = \dfrac{\sqrt{5}}{5}$	$\dfrac{4}{\sqrt{10}} = \dfrac{2\sqrt{5}}{10}$	$\dfrac{\sqrt{10}}{\sqrt{5}} = \sqrt{5}$	$\dfrac{12}{\sqrt{3}} = 4\sqrt{3}$	$\dfrac{1}{\sqrt{2}} = 2\sqrt{2}$
$\dfrac{4}{\sqrt{6}} = \dfrac{2\sqrt{6}}{3}$	$\dfrac{2}{\sqrt{3}} = \dfrac{2\sqrt{3}}{3}$	$\dfrac{3}{\sqrt{3}} = 3$	$\dfrac{a+\sqrt{a}}{\sqrt{a}} = \sqrt{a}+1$	$\dfrac{3}{\sqrt{2}} + \dfrac{1}{\sqrt{2}} = 2\sqrt{2}$
$\dfrac{\sqrt{2}}{\sqrt{3}} = \dfrac{\sqrt{3}}{3}$	$\dfrac{1}{4\sqrt{3}} = \dfrac{\sqrt{3}}{12}$	$\dfrac{2}{\sqrt{2a}} = \dfrac{\sqrt{2a}}{a}$	$\dfrac{5}{2\sqrt{3}} = \dfrac{5\sqrt{3}}{3}$	$\dfrac{2}{\sqrt{5}} + \dfrac{3}{\sqrt{5}} = \sqrt{5}$
$\dfrac{2a}{\sqrt{a}} = \sqrt{2a}$	$\dfrac{5}{\sqrt{2}} = \dfrac{\sqrt{10}}{2}$	$\dfrac{10}{\sqrt{5}} = 2\sqrt{5}$	$\dfrac{2}{\sqrt{10}} = 2$	$\dfrac{1}{\sqrt{2}} - \dfrac{1}{\sqrt{3}} = \dfrac{3\sqrt{2}-2\sqrt{3}}{6}$
$\dfrac{4}{\sqrt{2}} = \sqrt{2}$	$\dfrac{3}{\sqrt{7}} = \dfrac{7}{\sqrt{3}}$	$\dfrac{9}{\sqrt{3}} = 3\sqrt{3}$	$\dfrac{ab}{\sqrt{a}} = b\sqrt{a}$	$\dfrac{2\sqrt{3}}{\sqrt{2}} = \sqrt{6}$

4   What must you multiply $(\sqrt{5} - 2)$ by to get an answer of 1?

5   Show that $(1 + \sqrt{2})(1 - \sqrt{2}) = -1$

6 Indices and standard form

Homework 1

1 David says that the square of a number is always bigger than the number.
Is he correct?
Give a reason for your answer.

 2 Write these in index notation.
  a $6 \times 6 \times 6 \times 6 \times 6$ **d** 10
  b $2 \times 2 \times 2 \times 2 \times 2 \times 2 \times 2 \times 2 \times 2 \times 2$ **e** $\frac{1}{4}$
  c $17 \times 17 \times 17$ **f** $\left(\frac{1}{4}\right)^2$

 3 Find the value of each of the following.
  a 9^2 **d** 10^1 **g** 1^3 **j** 100^{-1}
  b 2^8 **e** 4^0 **h** 4^{-1} **k** $\left(\frac{1}{3}\right)^2$
  c 3^3 **f** 1000^0 **i** 5^{-3} **l** $\left(\frac{2}{3}\right)^2$

4 Find the value of each of the following.
  a 2^{20} **d** 8^3 **g** $2^{10} - 2^9$
  b 2^{21} **e** 5^{10} **h** $4^8 \times 2^{-16}$
  c 3^8 **f** -2^6 **i** $10^{51} \div 10^{49}$

 5 Simplify the following.

  a $3^8 \times 3^{11}$ **c** $\dfrac{3^7}{3^6}$ **e** $((1^2)^3)^4$

  b $12^4 \times 12^{-2}$ **d** $1.5^{10} \div 1.5^9$ **f** $(3.1^2)^{10}$

 6 Calculate:
  a $64^{\frac{1}{2}}$ **d** $27^{\frac{2}{3}}$ **g** $64^{\frac{1}{6}}$ **j** $1^{\frac{1}{5}}$
  b $169^{\frac{1}{2}}$ **e** $-27^{\frac{2}{3}}$ **h** $9^{-\frac{1}{2}}$ **k** $1^{-\frac{1}{5}}$
  c $125^{\frac{1}{3}}$ **f** $(-27)^{\frac{2}{3}}$ **i** $(-216)^{\frac{2}{3}}$

7 Use your calculator to work out the following.

    a 70^2 **b** $81^{-0.5}$ **c** $625^{1.5}$ **d** $10\,000^{-0.25}$

8 Simplify the following.

    a $a^5 \times a^3$ **c** $\dfrac{c^{11}}{c}$ **e** $q^{10} \div q^{11}$

    b $b^{10} \times b^6$ **d** $p^{100} \div p^{99}$ **f** $(s^2)^4$

9 Simplify the following.

    a $6x^3 \times 5x^6$ **b** $\dfrac{4a^9}{8a^5}$ **c** $5b^3 \times 2b^7$ <u>**d**</u> $(3b^4)^5$

<u>**10**</u> The number 256 can be written as 16^2 in index form.

Write down five other ways that 256 can be written in index form.

11 Tariq is investigating square numbers. He says that square numbers cannot end in a 2. Is he correct? Give a reason for your answer.

Homework 2

Apart from questions 6 and 8, this is a non-calculator exercise.

1 Write the following standard form numbers in ordinary form.

    a 8×10^2 **c** 4.0115×10^2 **e** 2.25×10^{-6}

    b 5.1×10^3 **d** 5×10^{-3}

2 Write the following ordinary form numbers in standard form.

    a 362 000   **c** 1 000 100   **e** 0.1

    b 45 500 000 000   **d** 0.000055

3 **Get Real!**

The distance of Saturn from the Sun is 1 429 400 000 km.

Write this distance in standard form.

4 Get Real!

The diameter of one molecule is 8.33×10^{-9} metres.

Write this number in ordinary form.

5 Get Real!

The following table shows the masses of the planets in the solar system.

Planet	Mass (kg)
Mercury	3.3×10^{23}
Venus	4.9×10^{24}
Earth	6.0×10^{24}
Mars	6.4×10^{23}
Jupiter	1.9×10^{27}
Saturn	5.7×10^{26}
Uranus	8.7×10^{25}
Neptune	1.0×10^{26}
Pluto	1.3×10^{22}

Place the planets in order of mass with the lightest first.

 6 Write the number 80^4 in standard form.

7 Calculate the following, giving your answers in standard form.

a $(4 \times 10^5) \times (2 \times 10^{11})$

b $(5 \times 10^3) \times (1.5 \times 10^9)$

c $(2.4 \times 10^5) \times (2 \times 10^{-6})$

d $\dfrac{4 \times 10^6}{2 \times 10^1}$

e $\dfrac{1.1 \times 10^6}{4.4 \times 10^{-3}}$

f $\dfrac{5.2 \times 10^5}{1.3 \times 10^8}$

 8 Use your calculator to find the following, giving your answers in standard form.

a $(4.1 \times 10^4) \times (2.2 \times 10^3)$

b $(5.8 \times 10^5) \times (2.3 \times 10^2)$

c $(2.12 \times 10^{-2}) \times (7.7 \times 10^{-6})$

d $(1.6 \times 10^4)^3$

e $\dfrac{4.4 \times 10^6}{2 \times 10^8}$

9 Given that $p = 4.5 \times 10^3$ and $q = 2 \times 10^{-1}$, calculate:

a $p \times q$ **c** $p + q$ **e** p^2

b $p \div q$ **d** $p - q$

7 Percentages

Homework 1

Calculate:

1 30% of 50 cm

2 15% of £70

3 75% of 9.6 m

4 $17\frac{1}{2}$% of £540

5 Work out the interest on £1000 for 2 years at $4\frac{1}{2}$% per annum.

6 Work out the amount if £500 is invested for 4 years at 3% per annum.

7 Get Real!
Todd is paid £350 per week.
He gets a 4% pay rise.
What is his new weekly pay?

8 Get Real!
A package holiday is priced at £760.
Julie gets a 10% discount for booking before the end of January.
How much does she pay?

9 Get Real!
Chris has 50 books on his shelves.
Jenny has 12% more books.
How many books has Jenny got?

10 Get Real!
A train ticket is priced at £48.
In the new year the cost increases by $2\frac{1}{2}$%.
What is the new cost of the train ticket?

Calculate:

11 84% of 35 kg

12 27% of 60 cm

13 130% of £35.50

14 $37\frac{1}{2}$% of £11.50

15 Work out the interest on £6520 for 4 years at 3.8% per annum.

16 Find the total owed if £3575 is borrowed for 3 years at 14.3% per annum.

17 **Get Real!**
Sarah's salary is £13 575 per year.
Her annual bonus is $1\frac{3}{4}$% of her salary.
How much does she earn altogether?

18 **Get Real!**
Jack sells computers.
He is paid commission of $8\frac{1}{4}$% on his sales.
Last year he sold computers worth £85 496.
How much was his commission?

Homework 2

1 A football team has a supporters club with 400 members.
45% of the members are female.
20% of the female members are over 50.
How many females over 50 belong to the club?

2 Sam earns £1100 per month.
On average, he spends 30% of this at AqaMart.
15% of his AqaMart spending is on frozen foods.
How much does Sam spend on frozen food?

3 There are 75 ducks on a lake.

40% of them are drakes.

70% of the drakes are mallards.

How many mallard drakes are on the lake?

4 Lisa bought a car for £20 000.

It depreciated by 30% in the first year and 35% in the second year.

What was it worth after two years?

5 Jake started a new job in March, on £250 per week.

After three months, he was given a pay rise of 24%.

In October, all employees were given a 5% pay rise.

What did Jake get paid in October?

6 Mathsville has 54 000 people eligible to vote.

65% of them voted in the last election.

37% of the votes cast were for Einstein.

How many votes did Einstein get?

7 Dan bought an antique table for £3785.

A year later, its value had gone up by 22%.

In the following year, its value went up by 33%.

What was the table worth at the end of the second year?

8 In 2003, HouseMasters sold 325 houses.

In 2004, their sales fell by 34%.

In 2005, sales went down again by $37\frac{1}{2}$%.

How many houses did they sell in 2005?

9 Aisha bought shares worth £4500.

A year later their value had fallen by 3.73%.

In the following year, their value went up by 3.14%.

What were the shares worth after two years?

10 If Aisha's shares went up by 3.73% in the second year, would they be worth £4500 again?

Explain your answer.

Homework 3

1 Find the compound interest on £300 invested for 2 years at 5% per annum.

2 Find the compound interest on £5000 invested for 2 years at 4% per annum.

3 £5000 is invested at 6% per annum compound interest.
Find the amount at the end of 2 years.

4 **a** £2000 is invested at 8% per annum compound interest.
Find the amount at the end of 3 years.

  b Compare this investment with the same principal earning simple interest at $5\frac{1}{2}$% per annum over the same period of time.

5 Find the compound interest on £750 invested for 4 years at 3% per annum.

6 Find the compound interest on £3500 invested for 3 years at 8.2% per annum.

7 £9000 is invested at $6\frac{1}{4}$% per annum compound interest.
Find the amount at the end of 5 years.

8 £4000 is invested at 7% per annum compound interest.
After how many years will this amount to more than £6000?

9 The population of Geometeria is 654 000 and is growing by 9% per annum each year.
How many years will it take for the population to reach a million?

Homework 4

1 Express 32p as a percentage of 40p.

2 Express 17 g as a percentage of 20 g.

3 Express 35p as a percentage of £5.

4 Express 4 mm as a percentage of 10 cm.

5 Express 22 cm as a percentage of half a metre.

6 Get Real!
The price of a packet of cereal goes up from £1.40 to £1.54

Find the percentage increase.

7 Get Real!
The rent on Jade's flat goes up from £80 per week to £84 per week.

Find the percentage increase.

8 Get Real!
In the autumn term, Sean scored 15 goals.

In the spring term he scored 21 goals.

Find the percentage increase.

9 Get Real!
In a spring sale, the price of a coat is reduced from £60 to £42.

Find the percentage reduction.

10 Get Real!
Tim bought 100 fluffy toys at 50p each.

He sold 65 of them at £1.20 each.

a How much did he pay for the toys?

b How much money did he get from selling the toys?

c Find the profit as a percentage of his costs.

11 Express 5 cm as a percentage of 14 cm.

12 Express £19.25 as a percentage of £44.

13 Express 39p as a percentage of £19.50

14 Express 216 g as a percentage of 4.8 kg.

15 Express 85 cm^2 as a percentage of 3 m^2.

16 Get Real!

The price of a hardback book is £15.

The paperback edition of the same book is £7.95

Express the difference as a percentage of the hardback price.

17 Get Real!

In March, Anna's sales totalled £44 000.

In April her sales were £36 960.

Find the percentage decrease.

18 Get Real!

Errol buys a car for £2450 and does some repairs.

He sells the car for £2950.

Find his percentage profit.

19 Get Real!

Kate bought 150 antique plates for £28 each.

She sold 98 of them for £54 each and a further 24 for £35 each.

a How much did it cost to buy the plates?

b How much money did she get from selling the plates?

c Find the profit as a percentage of her costs.

20 Get Real!

Tom bought a box of 60 old records for £40.

He sold 22 of them for £1.99 each.

Of these 14 were cracked and he sold the rest at three for a pound.

Calculate Tom's percentage profit.

Homework 5

1 Toys have been reduced by 20% in a sale.

Find the original price of these items.

a A doll priced at £4.80

b A train set priced at £12

c Wooden bricks priced at £6.80

2 Kylie has had a 10% pay rise.

She is now paid £264 per week.

How much was she paid before the rise?

3 Sarfraz is a car salesman.

In 2005 his sales amounted to £270 000.

This was an 8% increase on 2004.

What was his sales total in 2004?

4 The cost of Tara's train fare to work has gone up by $7\frac{1}{2}\%$.

It is now £2.58

What was her train fare before the rise?

5 The population of Toptown has gone up by 43% over the last 5 years.

It is now 50 765.

What was the population 5 years ago?

6 A plumber offers a 3% discount if customers pay him within 7 days.

Mrs Matheson paid £54.32 on the day after the job was done.

What was the bill before discount?

7 After other deductions, Gary pays tax on his wages at 22%.

His take-home pay is £214.50 per week.

What was his wage before tax was deducted?

8 Lucy has been promoted at work and has had two pay rises this year.

The first was 8% and the second was 5%.

Her annual salary is now £16 840.

What was her salary before the first pay rise?

Homework 1

 1 Simplify these ratios.

a $3:6$	**e** $3:18$	**i** $25:35$	**m** $0.6:0.4$
b $3:9$	**f** $3:21$	**j** $75:100$	**n** $3\frac{1}{2}:10\frac{1}{2}$
c $3:12$	**g** $14:28$	**k** $\frac{3}{4}:\frac{5}{6}$	**o** $25\%:75\%$
d $3:15$	**h** $9:36$	**l** $2.5:3.5$	**p** $75:200$

 2 **a** Write down three different pairs of numbers that are in the ratio $3:1$.

b Write down three different pairs of numbers that are in the ratio $5:1$.

c Explain how to find pairs of numbers that are in the ratio $5:1$.

d Harry writes the three pairs of numbers 16 and 20, 14 and 18, and 12 and 16. He says these pairs of numbers are all in the same ratio. Is Harry correct? Explain your answer.

 3 **Get Real!**

Ben's GCSE results are D, A, B, C, C, E, D, B and C.

What is the ratio of Ben's number of Grade C and above results to his number of below grade C results?

 4 **Get Real!**

In a large college, staffing costs are £15 million and other costs are £5 million. Find the ratio of staffing costs : other costs in its simplest form.

5 Get Real!

A recipe lists the following quantities of ingredients to make six scones.

Self-raising flour	240 grams
Salt	0.5 teaspoon
Sultanas	75 grams
Butter	40 grams
Caster sugar	25 grams
Egg	1 large
Milk	20 mℓ

a List the ingredients needed for 12 scones.

b How much flour would be needed for 15 scones?

 6 Get Real!

In a nursery, the number of children is 24 and the number of nurses is 4.

a What is the nurse : child ratio?

b Using this ratio, find how many nurses are needed for 30 children.

 7 Get Real!

Red and yellow paint are mixed in the ratio 2 : 5 to make the colour 'Hot Orange'.

a Which of these mixes will make 'Hot Orange' paint?

Amount of red paint (litres)	Amount of yellow paint (litres)
2	5
3	6
3	4
5	2
4	10
6	15
1	$2\frac{1}{2}$

b Write down another possible pair of amounts of red and yellow paint that would make 'Hot Orange'.

c Would it make any difference if the amounts were measured in pints instead of litres? Give a reason for your answer.

8 Get Real!

The aspect ratio of a film is the ratio of the width of the picture to its height. A common Cinemascope aspect ratio is 2.35 : 1.

Using this aspect ratio, find:

a the width of a picture if its height is 2 metres

b the height of a picture whose width is 4 metres.

9 The ratio $x : y$ simplifies to 2 : 9.

a If x is 6, what is y?

b If y is 36, what is x?

c If y is 13.5, what is x?

d If x and y add up to 55, what are x and y?

10 Make up another question like question **9** and give the answers.

11 Get Real!

a Find, in their simplest forms, the teacher : student ratios for these schools.

School	Number of teachers	Number of students
School 1	63	945
School 2	16	280
School 3	27	567
School 4	125	2275
School 5	55	880

b i If a school with 40 teachers had the same teacher : student ratio as School 1, how many students would it have?

ii If a school with 1500 students had the same teacher : student ratio as School 1, how many teachers would it have?

Homework 2

1 Divide these numbers and quantities in the ratio 1 : 4.

a 200   **c** £6.50   **e** £2.50

b 350   **d** 8 litres   **f** 3.5 litres

2 Divide the numbers and quantities in question **1** in the ratio 2 : 3.

3 Divide the numbers and quantities in question **1** in the ratio 7 : 3.

 4 Divide the numbers and quantities in question **1** in the ratio 1 : 4 : 5.

5 **Get Real!**

Salad dressing is made from oil and vinegar in the ratio 3 : 1.

a How much oil is needed to make 100 mℓ of salad dressing?

b How much vinegar is needed to make 0.4 litres of salad dressing?

c How much salad dressing can you make if you have plenty of oil but only 20 mℓ of vinegar?

6 **a** Find the number of boys and the number of girls in these schools.

School	Total number of students	Boy : girl ratio
School A	2000	1 : 1
School B	1800	2 : 7
School C	1860	2 : 3
School D	525	8 : 7
School E	1055	100 : 111

 b Find the boy : girl ratios in part **a** in the form 1 : n (in other words, find how many girls there are for every boy).

c Which school has the largest proportion of girls? Give a reason for your answer.

7 **a** Work out the amount of protein in 100 g of each of these foods.

Food	Carbohydrate : fat : protein ratio
Fudge biscuits	9 : 2 : 1
Strawberries	11 : 1 : 1
Scambled eggs	1 : 2 : 2
Chilli con carne	7 : 6 : 7
Italian sausage	1 : 5 : 4

b How many grams of chilli con carne do you need to eat to have 100 g of protein?

c How many grams of fudge biscuits do you need to eat to have 100 g of protein?

8 A school has £10 000 to spend on ICT equipment. The amount is to be split between the lower school and the upper school in the ratio of the number of students. There are 545 students in the lower school and 495 in the upper school.

How much money does each part of the school have to spend?

 9 Pen metal for pen nibs is an alloy of copper, gold and silver in the ratio $2:1:1$.

a How much of each metal is needed to make 1 kilogram of pen metal?

b If there are only 145 grams of gold left but plenty of copper and silver, how much pen metal can be made?

c How much gold would there be in a pen nib weighing 2 grams?

Homework 3

1 Get Real!

Jane pays £2.40 for 8 pencils.

How much would 20 of the same pencils cost?

2 Get Real!

Ali worked for 6 hours one day and earned £105.60

a How much will he be paid for a day when he works for 8 hours at the same rate of pay?

b Complete a copy of this table. Plot the values in the table as points on a graph, using the numbers of hours worked as the x-coordinates and the money earned as the corresponding y-coordinates.

Number of hours worked	0	2	4	6	8	10
Money earned (£)				105.60		

c The points should lie in a straight line through $(0, 0)$.

i Explain why.

ii What does the gradient of the line represent?

iii Show how to use the graph to find out how long Ali has to work to earn £100.

3 Get Real!

To make sandwiches for 3 people on 5 days, 750 g of meat is needed.

a How much meat is needed for sandwiches for 8 people on 1 day?

b How many days' sandwiches for 4 people will 600 g of meat make?

c Sandwiches for 5 people for 4 days needs the same amount of meat as sandwiches for 10 days for how many people?

4 Get Real!

Softouch hand cream is packed in small and large sizes, as shown in the table:

	Amount of hand cream	Price
Small size	55 grams	£1.05
Large size	225 grams	£4.35

Which size is better value for money?

Show how you worked out your answer.

5 Get Real!

A journey of 240 kilometres took 5 hours.

a How far would you go in 4 hours at the same average speed?

b How far would you go in three quarters of an hour at this average speed?

c How long would it take to travel 400 kilometres at this average speed?

6 Get Real!

A mail order company offers to supply and deliver boxes of

22 chocolates for £17.95

44 chocolates for £27.95

66 chocolates for £35.95.

a Which of these is the best value for money? Show how you worked it out.

b Write a sentence suggesting why there is such a difference in the price per chocolate.

7 Get Real!

Notice that the two parts of this question are really the same! Use part **a** to help you work out part **b**

a 75% of a number is 6. Use the unitary method to find 100% of the number.

b A T-shirt is £6 with the special offer (25% off). What was the original price of the T-shirt?

8 **a** Two numbers are in the ratio 1 : 0.6

The first number is 15; what is the second?

b Two numbers are in the ratio 1 : 0.6

The second number is 12; what is the first?

c Three numbers are in the ratio 1.2 : 1 : 0.8

The third number is 36; what are the other two numbers?

9 Get Real!

The weights of objects on other planets are proportional to their weights on Earth. A person weighing 150 pounds on Earth would weigh 60 pounds on Mercury and 160 pounds on Saturn.

a What would a person weighing 100 pounds on Earth weigh on Mercury?

b What would a mineral sample weighing 20 kilograms on Saturn weigh on Earth?

c Sketch a graph to show the weights of objects on Mercury compared with their weights on Earth.

d Express the ratio 'weight of object on Earth : weight of object on Mercury : weight of object on Saturn' as simply as you can.

Homework 4

1 At the beginning of 2000, Jack invested £740 in a savings account, which paid interest at an annual rate of 3.5%, and was added on to the account in December each year.

How much did Jack have in the account at the end of:

a 2000

b 2005?

c How much interest has Jack's money earned between the beginning of 2000 and the end of 2005?

Round your answers sensibly when necessary.

2 Angela's annual salary is £21 000. She expects to be given a rise of 1.8% of her salary every year.

a What will Angela's salary be after 2 years?

b What difference would it make to Angela's salary after 2 years if she were given a rise of 0.9% every six months instead of 1.8% a year?

3 Anne's savings in a building society account increase from £3400 to £3515.60 in one year.

   a What annual rate of interest is paid on Anne's account?

   b How much money will Anne have after 5 years if the building society continues to pay interest at this rate?

   c Anne wants her savings to exceed £5000. After how many years will this happen?

4 A population of bacteria is increasing in size by 5% every hour. There are 500 bacteria to begin with.

   Find, to the nearest 10, the number of bacteria after:

   a 2 hours

   b one and a half hours

   c 50 minutes

   d one day.

5 The mass of cells in a laboratory cell culture is doubling every 24 hours. At the start of the experiment, the mass of the cells is 25 grams.

   a Find the mass of the cells after:

   i 2 days

   ii a week

   iii 12 hours.

   b By how much is the mass of the cells multiplied after 12 hours?

   c Assuming the same growth rate, what was the mass of the cells 24 hours before the experiment started?

   d Write down a formula for the mass of the cells t days from the start of the experiment.

6 House prices are increasing at 5% a year.

   a What will be the price of a house costing £78 000 now in 2 years' time?

   b What would a house costing £100 000 now have been worth last year?

   c How realistic do you think it is to say that house prices go up by 5% a year?

7 John puts £100 into a savings account to which 2.5% interest is added every six months.

   a How much will John have in his account at the end of 1 year?

   b If instead, 5% interest had been added at the end of the year how much would be in his account?

   c After 3 years, how much more interest has John earned with 2.5% interest added twice a year than with 5% interest added once a year?

8 From the age of 2 years to the age of 5 years, the value of a car depreciates by 20% each year. Its value when it is 2 years old is £6500.

   a What will the car be worth when it is 3 years old?

   b What will the car be worth when it is 5 years old?

9 The radioactive isotope, Chromium 51, decays at such a rate that it loses half its mass every month.

   a What will be the mass of 10 kg of Chromium 51 after a year?

   b Estimate what percentage of its mass Chromium 51 loses each day. (Assume a month is 30 days.)

10 The radioactive isotope of carbon, Carbon 14, is used in carbon dating of ancient objects. The half-life of Carbon 14 is approximately 5700 years (that is, it takes 5700 years for any mass of Carbon 14 to decrease to half that mass).

   Sketch a graph to show how the mass of Carbon 14 decreases over many years.

Homework 5

1 y is proportional to the square of x (that is, $y = kx^2$) and when $x = 1$, $y = 4$.

   a Find the value of the constant k.

   b Find y when $x = 2$.

2 y is proportional to the square of x, and when $x = 5$, $y = 25$.

   a Write an equation showing the relationship between x and y.

   b Find the value of the constant in your equation.

   c Find x when:

   i $y = 64$ **ii** $y = 60$

3 Get Real!

   The cost, £C, of a railway journey is directly proportional to the distance travelled, d miles.

   A 20-mile journey costs £3.20

   a Find an equation connecting C and d.

   b Use your equation to find

   i the cost of a 105-mile journey

   ii the length of a journey costing £100.

4 **Get Real!**

The time, t hours, taken for a journey of a fixed length is inversely proportional to the average speed, v m.p.h., of the journey. When the average speed is 45 m.p.h., the time taken is 3 hours.

a Find how long the journey takes at an average speed of 40 m.p.h.

b Find the speed necessary to complete the journey in two and a half hours.

5 **Get Real!**

The number of days, d, needed to complete a business project is inversely proportional to the number of people, n, working on the project. It will take 10 people 3 days to do the work.

a Find an equation connecting d and n.

b How long will 5 people take to complete the project?

c How many people are needed to complete the project in 2 days?

d Sketch a graph of d against n.

6

Two variables, p and q, are such that p is directly proportional to q.

Which of the following statements are true?

a If q is doubled, p is halved.

b The graph of p against q is a straight line through the origin.

c q is inversely proportional to p.

d p and q satisfy an equation of the form $p = kq$.

7

One litre is equal to one and three quarter pints.

a Write a formula to find the number of litres, L, that are equivalent to P pints.

b Use your formula to draw a conversion graph for pints and litres and use the graph to convert 10 pints to litres.

c Write a sentence to show the proportional relationship between litres and pints.

8

Say what sort of proportion (direct proportion, inverse proportion or neither) exists between these variables.

a Circumference of circle and diameter.

b Time taken to complete a task and number of people available to do it.

c Area of square and square of its perimeter.

d Fahrenheit temperatures and corresponding Celsius temperatures.

e Number of weeks and the corresponding number of days.

f Number of glasses of water that can be poured from a bottle and the amount of water poured into each glass.

9 Write an algebraic statement for each of these relationships.

   a y is directly proportional to x.

   b The product of x and y is a constant.

   c y is proportional to the square of x.

   d y is inversely proportional to x.

Sketch a graph for each one.

10 Could x be directly proportional to y in this table?
Give a reason for your answer.

x	1	5	9	13
y	1.8	8.8	15.8	22.8

11 The area of the surface of a sphere is proportional to the square of its radius. A sphere of radius 10 cm has a surface area of 1257 cm^2.

   a What is the surface area of a sphere with a radius of:

     i 5 cm

     ii 20 cm?

   b Sketch a graph of the relationship.

12 The masses of two similar shapes are proportional to the cubes of their lengths. The first shape has a mass of 50 g and a length of 10 cm. The second has a mass of 100 g. Find its length.

13 Most conversion graphs express directly proportional relationships.

   a Give an example of such a conversion graph.

   b The conversion between Fahrenheit and Celsius temperatures does not represent a relationship of direct proportion. Explain this statement, drawing a sketch graph to illustrate your explanation.

9 Use of symbols

Homework 1

1 Multiply out the following.

a $2(x + 3)$

b $4(y + 4)$

c $2(t + 1)$

d $6(h - 2)$

e $3(d - 4)$

f $5(3ab + 2a)$

g $-2(x + 1)$

h $-3(p - 2)$

i $8(g - 2) + 4(g + 2)$

j $7(h + 2) + 3(2 - h)$

k $3(2 - a) - 4(a - 2)$

2 Expand:

a $p(p + 2)$

b $y(y + 4)$

c $b(2b + 3)$

d $g(g - 4)$

e $w(2w - 3)$

f $2k(3k + 4)$

g $5t(3t - 4)$

h $4a(2b - 3)$

i $2a(a + 1) + 4a(3 + a)$

j $3x(y + 2) + 2y(x - 1)$

k $\dfrac{y}{3}(6y - 1) + \dfrac{y}{6}(4 + 3y)$

3 Expand:

a $p^2(p^2 + 4)$

b $d^3(d^2 + 5)$

c $t^2(t^5 - 3)$

d $w^3(w^2 - 3)$

e $2a(3a^2 + 5)$

f $4p(4p - 3pq)$

g $3x^2y(2xy - 4xy^2)$

h $\dfrac{a}{2}(6ab - 2a)$

i $3xy^2z(2xz + 3yz)$

Homework 2

1 Expand and simplify:

a $(x + 4)(x + 2)$

b $(p + 3)(p + 4)$

c $(d - 2)(d + 5)$

d $(f - 2)(f - 6)$

e $(x + 2)^2$

f $(2x + 3)(x - 2)$

g $(3y + 2)(2y - 3)$

2 The answer is $x^2 - 2x + c$ where c is an integer. Find five expressions in the form $(x + a)(x + b)$ with this answer, stating the values of a, b and c each time.

3 Expand and simplify:

a $(2x + y)(x + 3y)$ **e** $(3x - y)(x - 2y)$ **i** $(3x + 2y)^2$

b $(3p + q)(3p + 2q)$ **f** $(2x - 4)(2x + 4)$ **j** $(5p - 2q)^2$

c $(3a - b)(2a + b)$ **g** $(6t - 2s)(3t - 4s)$

d $(4p + 2q)(3p - 2q)$ **h** $(a + b)^2$

Homework 3

1 Factorise:

a $5ab + 2b$ **e** $11ab - 7bc$ **i** $2p^2q + 5pq^2$

b $4pq + q$ **f** $p^2 + 3p$ **j** $3x^2yz^3 + 6xy^2z - 12xyz$

c $7ty + 10y$ **g** $2x^2 + xy$

d $3xz + 5x^2z$ **h** $4p^2 + 6pq$

2 Match the expression with the correct factorisation.
Fill in the missing expressions and factorisations.

Expression
$d^2 + 5d$
$3p^2q + 12pq^2$
$10a - 16$

Factorisation
$2(5a - 8)$
$5(d + 1)$
$4p^2q(q + 3)$

3 Factorise:

a $2x + 2y + x^2 + xy$ **c** $10p + 2q + 15p + 3q$ **e** $4(x + y)^2 + 3(x + y)$

b $ab + 3a + 2b + 6$ **d** $8d + 4 - 2d^2 - d$

Homework 4

1 Factorise:

a $y^2 + 7y + 6$ **e** $b^2 + 2b - 3$ **i** $x^2 - 36$

b $t^2 + t - 6$ **f** $x^2 + 4x - 32$ **j** $k^2 - 121$

c $p^2 - 5p - 6$ **g** $x^2 + 10x - 24$ **k** $x^2 - a^2$

d $x^2 - 10x + 9$ **h** $p^2 + 10d + 7$ **l** $8 - 2x - x^2$

> **HINT**
> One of these expressions cannot be factorised

2 Factorise:

a $2x^2 + 10x + 12$ **d** $7x^2 - 62x + 48$ **g** $a^2 - 16b^2$

b $3x^2 + 7x + 2$ **e** $4x^2 + 14x + 6$ **h** $2a^2 - 18b^2$

c $3x^2 + 3x - 6$ **f** $6x^2 - 10x - 4$

Homework 5

1 Simplify these expressions.

a $\dfrac{x^2 + 5x}{x + 5}$ **c** $\dfrac{x^2 + 8x + 7}{x + 1}$ **e** $\dfrac{x^2 + 4x - 5}{x^2 + 2x - 15}$

b $\dfrac{x^2 + 6x + 8}{x + 4}$ **d** $\dfrac{2(x - 2)^2}{(x - 2)}$

2 Simplify these expressions.

a $\dfrac{3x^2 + 5x + 2}{x + 1}$ **d** $\dfrac{x^2 + 2x}{x^2 - 4}$ **g** $\dfrac{5x^2 + 9x - 2}{2x^2 - 8}$

b $\dfrac{2x^2 + 7x + 6}{2x + 3}$ **e** $\dfrac{2x^2 - x - 6}{3x^2 - 5x - 2}$

c $\dfrac{x^2 - 9}{x + 3}$ **f** $\dfrac{3x^2 - x - 10}{9x^2 - 25}$

10 Quadratic graphs

Homework 1

  1 The graph shows the function $y = -x^2$ for values of x from -4 to 4.

Graph of $y = -x^2$

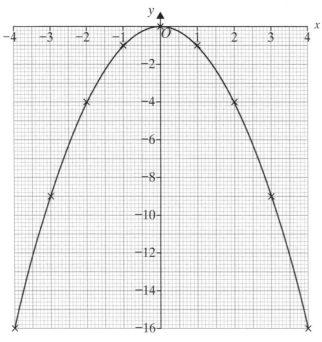

a Use the graph to estimate the value of:

    i -3.6^2 **ii** $-(-2.4)^2$

b Use the graph to find the values of x when:

    i $y = -11$ **ii** $y = -7.8$

2 **a** Copy and complete this table for $y = x^2 - 3$

x	−3	−2	−1	0	1	2	3
y		1	−2				6

b Draw the graph of $y = x^2 - 3$ for values of x from −3 to 3.

c Use your graph to find the value of y when:

   i $x = 1.6$ **ii** $x = -2.3$

d Use your graph to find the values of x when:

   i $y = 3.8$ **ii** $y = -1.4$

3 **a** Draw the graph of $y = 4x^2$

b Compare your graph with that of $y = -x^2$
What are the similarities and differences?

4 **a** Copy and complete the table for $y = 3x^2 + 1$

x	−4	−3	−2	−1	0	1	2	3	4
$3x^2$	48	29				3	12		
$y = 3x^2 + 1$	49	28				4	13		

b Draw the graph of $y = 3x^2 + 1$ for values of x from −4 to 4.

c Give the y-coordinate of the point on the curve with an x-coordinate of:

   i   3.5   **ii**   −2.4

d Give the x-coordinate of the points on the curve with a y-coordinate of:

   i   25   **ii**   7

5 **a** Draw the graph of $y = 2x^2 - 5$ for values of x from −4 to 4.

b Use your graph to find the value of y when:

   i $x = 1.3$ **ii** $x = -3.2$

c Use your graph to find the values of x when:

   i $y = 20$ **ii** $y = 9$

d Write the coordinates of the lowest point on the curve.

6 **a** Draw the graph of $y = 14 - x^2$ for values of x from −4 to 4.

b **i**   Give the x-coordinates of the points where the curve crosses the x-axis.

   ii Explain why the answers to part **i** are the square roots of 14.

7 **a** Copy and complete the table below, then use it to draw the graph of
$y = (x + 1)(4 - x)$

x	-2	-1	0	1	1.5	2	3	4	5
$x + 1$	-1				2.5		4		6
$4 - x$	6				2.5		1		-1
$y = (x + 1)(4 - x)$	-6				6.25		4		-6

b Write down the coordinates of the points where the curve crosses the x-axis.

 8 **a** Draw a table and a graph for $y = x(x + 2)$ for values of x from -4 to 2.

b Write down the coordinates of the points where the curve crosses the x-axis.

 9 **Get Real!**

When a stone is dropped from a high bridge over a river, the
height of the stone above the water, h metres, after t seconds
is given by the formula $h = 76 - 5t^2$

a Draw the graph of $h = 76 - 5t^2$ for $0 \leqslant t \leqslant 4$

b Use your graph to find:

   i the height of the stone after 1.5 seconds

   ii the time when the stone is 20 metres above the water

   iii the time when the stone hits the water.

h metres

water

10 The graph shows the points that Cliff has plotted for his graph of $y = 2x^2$

Graph of $y = 2x^2$

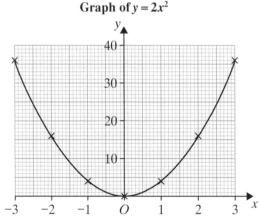

a Is Cliff correct?

b Give a reason for your answer.

11 The graphs of three quadratic functions are shown in the sketch.

The functions are

$$y = x^2 + 5 \qquad y = 5x^2 \qquad y = -5x^2$$

Choose the function that represents each curve.

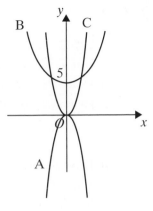

12 a On separate axes draw the graphs of:

i $y = (2+x)(4+x)$ **iii** $y = (2+x)(4-x)$

ii $y = (2-x)(4-x)$ **iv** $y = (2-x)(4+x)$

b What do you notice about your graphs?

13 a Give four possible equations for graph A.

    b Give four possible equations for graph B.

Homework 2

1 a Copy and complete this table for $y = x^2 + 2x$

x	−4	−3	−2	−1	0	1	2
y	8	3		−1		3	

b Draw the graph of $y = x^2 + 2x$ for values of x from −4 to 2.

c Use your graph to solve the equation $x^2 + 2x = 0$

d i Draw the line $y = 7$ on your graph.

    ii Find the x-coordinates of the points where the line $y = 7$ crosses the curve $y = x^2 + 2x$

    iii Write down the quadratic equation whose solutions are the answers to part **ii**.

2 **a** Copy and complete this table for $y = x^2 - 2x + 1$

x	−2	−1	0	1	2	3	4
y	9				1	4	

b Draw the graph of $y = x^2 - 2x + 1$ for values of x from −2 to 4.

c i Write down the x-coordinate of the point where the curve meets the x-axis.

ii Write down the quadratic equation whose solution is the answer to part **i**.

d i Write the x-coordinates of the points where the line $y = 5$ crosses the graph of $y = x^2 - 2x + 1$

ii Write a quadratic equation whose solutions are the answers to part **i**.

 3 **a** Copy and complete this table for $y = 10 - x - x^2$

x	−4	−3	−2	−1	−0.5	0	1	2	3
y		4			10.25			4	

b Draw the graph of $y = 10 - x - x^2$ for values of x from −4 to 3.

c i Find the x-coordinates of the points where the graph crosses the line $y = 0$

ii Write down the quadratic equation whose solutions are the answers to part **i**.

d Use your graph to find the solutions of:

i $4 - x - x^2 = 0$ **ii** $x^2 + x = 3$ **iii** $x^2 + x - 7 = 0$

 4 **a** Draw the graph of $y = 2x^2 + x - 7$ for values of x from −4 to 4.

b i Write the x-values where the curve crosses the x-axis.

ii Write the quadratic equation whose solutions are the answers to part **i**.

c i Write the x-values where the curve meets the line $y = 15$

ii Write a quadratic equation whose solutions are the answers to part **i**.

5 Get Real!

When a car does an emergency stop, the distance it travels in coming to a halt is related to its speed by the formula:

$d = 0.015v^2 + 0.3v$ where d is the distance in metres
and v is the speed in miles per hour.

a Draw a graph of d against v for values of v from 0 to 70.

b Use your graph to estimate the distance it would take to stop if the car was travelling at:

  i 25 mph   **ii** 35 mph   **iii** 53 mph   **iv** 68 mph.

c Use your graph to estimate how fast a car can travel and be able to stop in:

  i 10 m   **ii** 25 m   **iii** 75 m.

6 A teacher asks her class to draw up a table for $y = 6 - 4x - x^2$

a This is Kylie's table.

Kylie's table

x	−3	−2	−1	0	1	2	3
6	6	6	6	6	6	6	6
$-4x$	+12	+8	+4	0	−4	−8	−12
$-x^2$	+9	+4	+1	0	+1	+4	+9
$y = 6 - 4x - x^2$	27	18	11	6	3	2	3

  i Are any of Kylie's y-values correct?

  ii Explain any mistakes she has made.

b This is Will's table.

Will's table

x	−3	−2	−1	0	1	2	3
6	6	6	6	6	6	6	6
$-4x$	−12	−8	−4	0	−4	−8	−12
$-x^2$	−9	−4	−1	0	−1	−4	−9
$y = 6 - 4x - x^2$	−15	−6	1	6	1	−6	−15

  i Are any of Will's y-values correct?

  ii Explain any mistakes he has made.

7 **a** Draw the graph of $y = 5x^2 + 4x - 8$ for $-3 \leqslant x \leqslant +2$

  b Use your graph to solve the following equations.

    i $5x^2 + 4x - 8 = 0$ **ii** $5x^2 + 4x - 8 = 10$ **iii** $5x^2 + 4x = 0$

  c Emma says that the equation $5x^2 + 4x - 8 = -10$ cannot be solved.

    i Is she correct?   **ii** Give a reason for your answer.

8 **a** Draw the graph of $y = 9 + 5x - 3x^2$ for $-2 \leqslant x \leqslant 4$

   b **i** Write down the solutions of the equation $9 + 5x - 3x^2 = 0$

   ii Explain how you found the solutions and why your method works.

   c **i** Use your graph to solve the equation $3x^2 = 5x + 6$

   ii Explain how you found the solutions and why your method works.

 9 **a** Draw the graph of $y = 3x(2 - x)$ for values of x from -1 to 3.

   b For what value of c does the equation $6x - 3x^2 = c$ have just one solution?

   c **i** Describe the values of c for which the equation $3x - 3x^2 = c$ has no solutions.

   ii Give a reason for your answer.

Homework 3

In questions **1** to **6** draw graphs for $-4 \leqslant x \leqslant +4$ to solve the simultaneous equations.

 1 $y = x + 4$
$y = x^2$

3 $y = 3x + 1$
$y = -x^2$

5 $y = 2x$
$y = 3x^2 - 2$

2 $y = 2x$
$y = x^2 - 5$

4 $x + y = 7$
$y = 2x^2$

6 $x - y + 4 = 0$
$y = x(x - 1)$

 7 **a** On the same axes draw the graphs of $y = 5 + 2x - x^2$ and $y = x + 1$ for $-2 \leqslant x \leqslant +4$

   b Use your graph to solve the simultaneous equations $y = 5 + 2x - x^2$ and $y = x + 1$

   c Write down and simplify the quadratic equation whose solutions are given by the x-coordinates of the points of intersection of the graphs.

   d How can you tell from the graph that the simultaneous equations $y = 5 + 2x - x^2$ and $y = x + 7$ have no solutions?

8 **a** Draw the graph of $y = 3x^2 - 7x + 6$ for $-1 \leqslant x \leqslant +3$

b By drawing other lines on your graph, use it to find the solutions of these pairs of simultaneous equations.

i $\quad y = 3x^2 - 7x + 6$ **ii** $\quad y = 3x^2 - 7x + 6$ **iii** $\quad y = 3x^2 - 7x + 6$

$\qquad y = 5 - x$ $y = 3 - x$ $y = 1 - x$

9 **a** Draw the graph of $y = x^2$ for $-4 \leqslant x \leqslant +4$

b By drawing other lines on your graph, use it to solve these quadratic equations.

i $\quad x^2 + 2x = 0$ **ii** $\quad x^2 - 2x - 1 = 0$ **iii** $\quad x^2 + 3x - 2 = 0$

Remember to write down the equations of your other lines.

10 **a** Complete the table of values for $y = x^2 - 3x - 3$

x	-2	-1	0	1	2	3	4
y	7		-3		-5		1

b Draw the graph of $y = x^2 - 3x - 3$ for values of x between -2 and 4.

c Write down the solutions of $x^2 - 3x - 3 = 0$

d Find graphically the solutions of $x^2 - 3x - 3 = x - 6$

11 **a** Complete the table of values for $y = x^2 - 2x - 4$

x	-2	-1	0	1	2	3	4
y			-4			-1	4

b Draw the graph of $y = x^2 - 2x - 4$ for values of x between -2 and 4.

c Write down the solutions of $x^2 - 2x - 4 = 0$

d By drawing an appropriate linear graph write down the solutions of

$\qquad x^2 - 3x - 2 = 0$

12 Trudi says that you can solve the quadratic equation $3x^2 - 7x + 1 = 0$ by finding the points of intersection of the graphs of $y = 3x^2$ and $y = 1 - 7x$ Is she correct? Give a reason for your answer.

13 Work out which graph you would draw on the graph of $y = 4x^2$ to solve each of these equations:

a $4x^2 - 3x - 5 = 0$ **c** $11 - 4x^2 = 3x$

b $2x^2 + x - 3 = 0$ **d** $x^2 - 2x = 1$

14 **Get Real!**

A bus passes a layby just as a car pulls out to travel in the same direction.

The following equations give for each vehicle the distance, d metres, travelled in the next t seconds.

Bus: $d = 15t$

Car: $d = 6t + 0.25t^2$

a Draw a graph showing $d = 15t$ and $d = 6t + 0.25t^2$ for $0 \leqslant x \leqslant 40$

b Write the coordinates of the point of intersection of the graphs and explain the significance of these values in this context.